From an etching by Chifflact

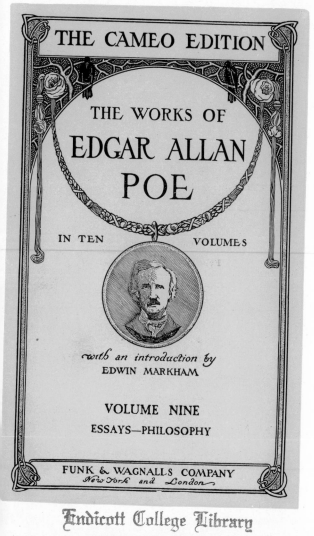

THE CAMEO EDITION

THE WORKS OF
EDGAR ALLAN POE

IN TEN VOLUMES

with an introduction by
EDWIN MARKHAM

VOLUME NINE
ESSAYS—PHILOSOPHY

FUNK & WAGNALLS COMPANY
New York and London

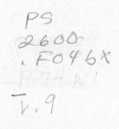

VOLUME IX

ESSAYS—PHILOSOPHY

CONTENTS

EUREKA

AN ESSAY ON

THE MATERIAL AND SPIRITUAL UNIVERSE

———

[Published as "Eureka: A Prose Poem," Geo. P. Putnam, New York, 1848, and dedicated to Alexander von Humboldt.]

———

[To the few who love me and whom I love—to those who feel rather than to those who think—to the dreamers and those who put faith in dreams as in the only realities—I offer this Book of Truths, not in its character of Truth-Teller, but for the Beauty that abounds in its Truth; constituting it true. To these I present the composition as an Art-Product alone:—let us say as a Romance; or, if I be not urging too lofty a claim, as a Poem.

What I here propound is true:—therefore it cannot die:—or if by any means it be now trodden down so that it die, it will "rise again to the Life Everlasting."

Nevertheless it is as a Poem only that I wish this work to be judged after I am dead.]

IT is with humility really unassumed—it is with a sentiment even of awe—that I pen the opening sentence of this work: for of all conceivable subjects I approach the reader with the most solemn—the most comprehensive—the most difficult—the most august.

What terms shall I find sufficiently simple in their sublimity—sufficiently sublime in their

5

simplicity—for the mere enunciation of my theme?

I design to speak of the *Physical, Metaphysical and Mathematical—of the Material and Spiritual Universe:—of its Essence, its Origin, its Creation, its Present Condition and its Destiny.* I shall be so rash, moreover, as to challenge the conclusions, and thus, in effect, to question the sagacity, of many of the greatest and most justly reverenced of men.

In the beginning, let me as distinctly as possible announce—not the theorem which I hope to demonstrate—for, whatever the mathematicians may assert, there is, in this world at least, *no such thing* as demonstration—but the ruling idea which, throughout this volume, I shall be continually endeavoring to suggest.

My general proposition, then, is this:—*In the Original Unity of the First Thing lies the Secondary Cause of All Things, with the Germ of their Inevitable Annihilation.*

In illustration of this idea, I propose to take such a survey of the Universe that the mind may be able to receive and to perceive an individual impression.

He who from the top of Ætna casts his eyes leisurely around, is affected chiefly by the *extent* and *diversity* of the scene. Only by a rapid whirling on his heel could he hope to comprehend the panorama in the sublimity of its *oneness*. But as, on the summit of Ætna, *no* man has thought of whirling on his heel, so no man has ever taken into his brain the full uniqueness of the prospect; and so, again, whatever considerations lie involved in this uniqueness, have as yet no practical existence for mankind.

I do not know a treatise in which a survey of the *Universe*—using the word in its most comprehensive and only legitimate acceptation—is taken at all:—and it may be as well here to mention that by the term "Universe," wherever employed without qualification in this essay, I mean to designate *the utmost conceivable expanse of space, with all things, spiritual and material, that can be imagined to exist within the compass of that expanse.* In speaking of what is *ordinarily* implied by the expression, "Universe," I shall take a phrase of limitation—"the Universe of stars." Why this distinction is considered necessary, will be seen in the sequel.

But even of treatises on the really limited, although always assumed as the *unlimited*, Universe of *stars*, I know none in which a survey, even of this limited Universe, is so taken as to warrant deductions from its *individuality.* The nearest approach to such a work is made in the "Cosmos" of Alexander von Humboldt. He presents the subject, however, *not* in its individuality but in its generality. His theme, in its last result, is the law of *each* portion of the merely physical Universe, as this law is related to the laws of *every other* portion of this merely physical Universe. His design is simply synæretical. In a word, he discusses the universality of material relation, and discloses to the eye of Philosophy whatever inferences have hitherto lain hidden *behind* this universality. But however admirable be the succinctness with which he has treated each particular point of his topic, the mere multiplicity of these points occasions, necessarily, an amount of detail, and thus an involution of idea, which preclude all *individuality* of impression.

It seems to me that, in aiming at this latter effect, and, through it, at the consequences—the conclusions—the suggestions—the speculations—or, if nothing better offer itself, the mere guesses which may result from it—we require something like a mental gyration on the heel. We need so rapid a revolution of all things about the central point of sight that, while the minutiæ vanish altogether, even the more conspicuous objects become blended into one. Among the vanishing minutiæ, in a survey of this kind, would be all exclusively terrestrial matters. The Earth would be considered in its planetary relations alone. A man, in this view, becomes mankind; mankind a member of the cosmical family of Intelligences.

And now, before proceeding to our subject proper, let me beg the reader's attention to an extract or two from a somewhat remarkable letter,* which appears to have been found corked in a bottle and floating on the *Mare Tenebrarum*—an ocean well described by the Nubian geographer, Ptolemy Hephestion, but little frequented in modern days unless by the Transcen-

---

* See tale, " Mellonta Tauta," vol. III., present edition. — EDITOR.

dentalists and some other divers for crotchets.
The date of this letter, I confess, surprises me
even more particularly than its contents; for it
seems to have been written in the year *two* thousand eight hundred and forty-eight. As for the
passages I am about to transcribe, they, I fancy,
will speak for themselves.

"Do you know, my dear friend," says the
writer, addressing, no doubt, a contemporary—
"Do you know that it is scarcely more than eight
or nine hundred years ago since the metaphysicians first consented to relieve the people of the
singular fancy that there exist *but two practicable roads to Truth?* Believe it if you can! It
appears, however, that long, long ago, in the
night of Time, there lived a Turkish philosopher
called Aries and surnamed Tottle." [Here, possibly, the letter-writer means Aristotle; the best
names are wretchedly corrupted in two or three
thousand years.] "The fame of this great man
depended mainly upon his demonstration that
sneezing is a natural provision, by means of
which over-profound thinkers are enabled to expel superfluous ideas through the nose; but he
obtained a scarcely less valuable celebrity as the
founder, or at all events as the principal propa-
gator, of what was termed the *de*ductive or *a
priori* philosophy. He started with what he
maintained to be axioms, or self-evident
truths:—and the now well-understood fact that
no truths are *self*-evident, really does not make
in the slightest degree against his speculations:—
it was sufficient for his purpose that the truths in

question were evident at all. From axioms he proceeded, logically, to results. His most illustrious disciples were one Tuclid, a geometrician," [meaning Euclid] "and one Kant, a Dutchman, the originator of that species of Transcendentalism which, with the change merely of a C for a K, now bears his peculiar name.

"Well, Aries Tottle flourished supreme, until the advent of one Hog, surnamed 'the Ettrick shepherd,' who preached an entirely different system, which he called the *a posteriori* or *inductive*. His plan referred altogether to sensation. He proceeded by observing, analyzing, and classifying facts—*instantiæ Naturæ*, as they were somewhat affectedly called—and arranging them into general laws. In a word, while the mode of Aries rested on *noumena*, that of Hog depended on *phenomena;* and so great was the admiration excited by this latter system that, at its first introduction, Aries fell into general disrepute. Finally, however, he recovered ground, and was permitted to divide the empire of Philosophy with his more modern rival:—the savans contenting themselves with proscribing all *other* competitors, past, present, and to come; putting an end to all controversy on the topic by the promulgation of a Median law, to the effect that the Aristotelian and Baconian roads are, and of right ought to be, the sole possible avenues to knowledge:—'Baconian,' you must know, my dear friend," adds the letter-writer at this point, "was an adjective invented as equivalent to Hog-ian, and at the same time more dignified and euphonious.

"Now I do assure you most positively"—proceeds the epistle—"that I represent these matters fairly; and you can easily understand how restrictions so absurd on their very face must have operated, in those days, to retard the progress of true Science, which makes its most important advances—as all History will show—by seemingly intuitive *leaps*. These ancient ideas confined investigation to crawling; and I need not suggest to you that crawling, among varieties of locomotion, is a very capital thing of its kind;—but because the tortoise is sure of foot, for this reason must we clip the wings of the eagles? For many centuries, so great was the infatuation, about Hog especially, that a virtual stop was put to all thinking, properly so called. No man dared utter a truth for which he felt himself indebted to his soul alone. It mattered not whether the truth was even demonstrably such; for the dogmatizing philosophers of that epoch regarded only *the road* by which it professed to have been attained. The end, with them, was a point of no moment, whatever:—'the means!' they vociferated—'let us look at the means!'—and if, on scrutiny of the means, it was found to come neither under the category Hog, nor under the category Aries (which means ram), why then the savans went no farther, but, calling the thinker a fool and branding him a 'theorist,' would never, thenceforward, have any thing to do either with *him* or with his truths.

"Now, my dear friend," continued the letter-writer, "it cannot be maintained that by the crawling system exclusively adopted, men would arrive at the maximum amount of truth, even in any long series of ages; for the repression of imagination was an evil not to be counterbalanced even by *absolute* certainty in the snail processes.   But their certainty was very far from absolute.   The error of our progenitors was quite analogous with that of the wiseacre who fancies he must necessarily see an object the more distinctly, the more closely he holds it to his eyes.   They blinded themselves, too, with the impalpable, titillating Scotch snuff of *detail;* and thus the boasted facts of the Hog-ites were by no means always facts—a point of little importance but for the assumption that they always *were.*   The vital taint, however, in Baconianism —its most lamentable fount of error—lay in its tendency to throw power and consideration into the hands of merely perceptive men—of those inter-Tritonic minnows, the microscopical savans —the diggers and pedlers of minute *facts,* for the most part in physical science—facts, all of which they retailed at the same price upon the highway;   their value depending, it was supposed, simply upon the *fact of their fact,* without reference to their applicability or inapplicability in the development of those ultimate and only legitimate facts, called Law.

"Than the persons"—the letter goes on to say —"than the persons thus suddenly elevated by the Hog-ian philosophy into a station for which they were unfitted—thus transferred from the sculleries into the parlors of Science—from its pantries into its pulpits—than these individuals a more intolerant—a more intolerable set of bigots and tyrants never existed on the face of the earth. Their creed, their text, and their sermon were, alike, the one word *'fact'*—but, for the most part, even of this one word, they knew not even the meaning. On those who ventured to *disturb* their facts with the view of putting them in order and to use, the disciples of Hog had no mercy whatever. All attempts at generalization were met at once by the words 'theoretical,' 'theory,' 'theorist'—all *thought,* to be brief, was very properly resented as a personal affront to themselves. Cultivating the natural sciences to the exclusion of Metaphysics, the Mathematics, and Logic, many of these Baconengendered philosophers—one-idead, one-sided, and lame of a leg—were more wretchedly helpless—more miserably ignorant, in view of all the comprehensible objects of knowledge, than the veriest unlettered hind who proves that he knows something at least, in admitting that he knows absolutely nothing.

"Nor had our forefathers any better right to talk about *certainty,* when pursuing, in blind confidence, the *a priori* path of axioms, or of the Ram. At innumerable points this path was scarcely as straight as a ram's-horn. The simple truth is, that the Aristotelians erected their castles upon a basis far less reliable than air; *for no such things as axioms ever existed or can pos-*

sibly exist at all.   This they must have been very blind indeed not to see, or at least to suspect; for even in their own day, many of their long-admitted 'axioms' had been abandoned: *'ex nihilo nihil fit,'* for example, and a 'thing cannot act where it is not,' and 'there cannot be antipodes,' and 'darkness cannot proceed from light.' These and numerous similar propositions formerly accepted, without hesitation, as axioms, or undeniable truths, were, even at the period of which I speak, seen to be altogether untenable:— how absurd in these people, then, to persist in relying upon a basis, as immutable, whose mutability had become so repeatedly manifest!

"But, even through evidence afforded by themselves against themselves, it is easy to convict these *a priori* reasoners of the grossest unreason—it is easy to show the futility—the impalpability of their axioms in general.   I have now lying before me"—it will be observed that we still proceed with the letter—"I have now lying before me a book printed about a thousand years ago.   Pundit assures me that it is decidedly the cleverest ancient work on its topic, which is 'Logic.'   The author, who was much esteemed in his day, was one Miller, or Mill; and we find it recorded of him, as a point of some importance, that he rode a mill-horse whom he called Jeremy Bentham:—but let us glance at the volume itself.

"Ah!—'Ability or inability to conceive,' says Mr. Mill, very properly, 'is *in no case* to be received as a criterion of axiomatic truth.'   Now, that this is a palpable truism, no one in his senses will deny. *Not* to admit the proposition, is to insinuate a charge of variability in Truth itself, whose very title is a synonym of the Steadfast. If ability to conceive be taken as a criterion of Truth, then a truth to *David* Hume would very seldom be a truth to *Joe;* and ninety-nine hundredths of what is undeniable in Heaven, would be demonstrable falsity upon Earth. The proposition of Mr. Mill, then, is sustained. I will not grant it to be an *axiom;* and this merely because I am showing that *no* axioms exist; but, with a distinction which could not have been cavilled at even by Mr. Mill himself, I am ready to grant that, *if* an axiom *there be,* then the proposition of which we speak has the fullest right to be considered an axiom—that no *more* absolute axiom *is*—and, consequently, that any subsequent proposition which shall conflict with this one primarily advanced, must be either a falsity in itself—that is to say, no axiom—or, if admitted axiomatic, must at once neutralize both itself and its predecessor.

"And now, by the logic of their own propounder, let us proceed to test any one of the axioms propounded. Let us give Mr. Mill the fairest of play. We will bring the point to no ordinary issue. We will select for investigation no common-place axiom—no axiom of what, not the less preposterously because only impliedly, he terms his secondary class—as if a positive truth by definition could be either more or less positively a truth: we will select, I say, no axiom of an unquestionability so questionable as is

to be found in Euclid. We will not talk, for example, about such propositions as that two
straight lines cannot enclose a space, or that the
whole is greater than any one of its parts. We
will afford the logician *every* advantage. We will
come at once to a proposition which he regards as
the acme of the unquestionable—as the quintessence of axiomatic undeniability. Here it is:—
'Contradictions cannot *both* be true—that is,
cannot coexist in nature.' Here Mr. Mill means
for instance,—and I give the most forcible instance conceivable,—that a tree must be either a
tree or *not* a tree—that it cannot be at the
same time a tree *and* not a tree: all which is
quite reasonable of itself, and will answer re-
markably well as an axiom, until we bring it into
collation with an axiom insisted upon a few
pages before; in other words—words which I
have previously employed—until we test it by
the logic of its own propounder. 'A tree,' Mr.
Mill asserts, 'must be either a tree or *not* a tree.'
Very well: and now let me ask him, *why*. To
this little query there is but one response—I defy
any man living to invent a second. The sole answer is this:—'Because we find it *impossible to
conceive* that a tree can be anything else than a
tree or not a tree.' This, I repeat, is Mr. Mill's
sole answer—he will not *pretend* to suggest another; and yet, by his own showing, his answer is
clearly no answer at all—for has he not already
required us to admit, *us an axiom*, that ability or
inability to conceive, is *in no case* to be taken as a
criterion of axiomatic truth? Thus all—absolute-

ly *all* his argumentation is at sea without a rudder. Let it not be urged that an exception from the general rule is to be made, in cases where the 'impossibility to conceive' is so peculiarly great as when we are called upon to conceive a tree *both* a tree and *not* a tree. Let no attempt, I say, be made at urging this sotticism; for, in the first place, there are no *degrees* of 'impossibility,' and thus no one impossible conception can be *more* peculiarly impossible than another impossible conception: in the second place, Mr. Mill himself—no doubt after thorough deliberation—has most distinctly, and most rationally, excluded all opportunity for exception, by the emphasis of his proposition, that, *in no case,* is ability or inability to conceive, to be taken as a criterion of axiomatic truth: in the third place, even were exceptions admissible at all, it remains to be shown how any exception is admissible *here.* That a tree can be both a tree and not a tree, is an idea which the angels, or the devils, *may* entertain, and which no doubt many an earthly Bedlamite, or Transcendentalist, *does.*

"Now I do not quarrel with these ancients," continues the letter-writer, "*so much* on account of the transparent frivolity of their logic—which, to be plain, was baseless, worthless, and fantastic altogether—as on account of their pompous and infatuate proscription of all *other* roads to Truth than the two narrow and crooked paths—the one of creeping and the other of crawling—to which, in their ignorant perversity, they have dared to confine the Soul—the Soul

IX. 2

which loves nothing so well as to soar in those regions of illimitable intuition which are utterly incognizant of *'path.'*

"By the by, my dear friend, is it not an evidence of the mental slavery entailed upon those bigoted people by their Hogs and Rams, that in spite of the eternal prating of their savans about *roads* to Truth, none of them fell, even by accident, into what we now so distinctly perceive to be the broadest, the straightest, and most available of all mere roads—the great thoroughfare—the majestic highway of the *Consistent?* Is it not wonderful that they should have failed to deduce from the works of God the vitally momentous consideration that *a perfect consistency can be nothing but an absolute truth?* How plain—how rapid our progress since the late announcement of this proposition! By its means, investigation has been taken out of the hands of the groundmoles, and given as a duty, rather than as a task, to the true—to the *only* true thinkers—to the generally-educated men of ardent imagination. These latter—our Keplers—our Laplaces—'speculate'—'theorize'—these are the terms—can you not fancy the shout of scorn with which they would be received by our progenitors, were it possible for them to be looking over my shoulders as I write? The Keplers, I repeat, speculate—theorize—and their theories are merely corrected—reduced—sifted—cleared, little by little, of their chaff of inconsistency—until at length there stands apparent an unencumbered *Consistency*—a consistency which the most stolid admit—because it *is* a consistency—to be an absolute and unquestionable *Truth*.

"I have often thought, my friend, that it must have puzzled these dogmaticians of a thousand years ago, to determine, even, by which of their two boasted roads it is that the cryptographist attains the solution of the more complicated cyphers—or by which of them Champollion guided mankind to those important and innumerable truths which, for so many centuries, have lain entombed amid the phonetical hieroglyphics of Egypt. In especial, would it not have given these bigots some trouble to determine by which of their two roads was reached the most momentous and sublime of *all* their truths—the truth—the fact of *gravitation?* Newton deduced it from the laws of Kepler. Kepler admitted that these laws he *guessed*— these laws whose investigation disclosed to the greatest of British astronomers that principle, the basis of all (existing) physical principles, in going behind which we enter at once the nebulous kingdom of metaphysics. Yes!—these vital laws Kepler *guessed*—that is to say, he *imagined* them. Had he been asked to point out either the *de*ductive or *in*ductive route by which he attained them, his reply might have been—'I know nothing about *routes*—but I *do* know the machinery of the Universe. Here it is. I grasped it with *my soul*—I reached it through mere dint of *intuition*.' Alas, poor ignorant old man! Could not any metaphysician have told him that what he called 'intuition' was but the conviction re-

sulting from *deductions* or *inductions* of which
the processes were so shadowy as to have escaped
his consciousness, eluded his reason, or bidden
defiance to his capacity of expression? How
great a pity it is that some 'moral philosopher'
had not enlightened him about all this! How it
would have comforted him on his death-bed to
know that, instead of having gone intuitively,
and thus unbecomingly, he had, in fact, proceeded decorously and legitimately—that is to say
Hog-ishly, or at least Ram-ishly—into the vast
halls where lay gleaming, untended, and hitherto
untouched by mortal hand—unseen by mortal
eye—the imperishable and priceless secrets of the
Universe!

"Yes, Kepler was essentially a *theorist;* but
this title, *now* of so much sanctity, was, in those
ancient days, a designation of supreme con-
tempt. It is only *now* that men begin
to appreciate that divine old man—to sym-
pathize with the prophetical and poetical
rhapsody of his ever memorable words. For
my part," continues the unknown correspondent,
"I glow with a sacred fire when I even think of
them, and feel that I shall never grow weary of
their repetition:—in concluding this letter, let
me have the real pleasure of transcribing them
once again:—'*I care not whether my work be
read now or by posterity. I can afford to wait a
century for readers when God himself has waited
six thousand years for an observer. I triumph.
I have stolen the golden secret of the Egyptians.
I will indulge my sacred fury.'* "

Here end my quotations from this very unaccountable and, perhaps, somewhat impertinent epistle; and perhaps it would be folly to comment, in any respect, upon the chimerical, not to say revolutionary, fancies of the writer—whoever he is—fancies so radically at war with the well-considered and well-settled opinions of this age. Let us proceed, then, to our legitimate thesis, *The Universe.*

This thesis admits a choice between two modes of discussion:—We may *ascend* or *descend.* Beginning at our own point of view, at the Earth on which we stand, we may pass to the other planets of our system, thence to the Sun, thence to our system considered collectively, and thence, through other systems, indefinitely outwards; or, commencing on high at some point as definite as we can make it or conceive it, we may come down to the habitation of Man. Usually, that is to say, in ordinary essays on Astronomy, the first of these two modes is, with certain reservation, adopted: this for the obvious reason that astronomical *facts*, merely, and principles, being the object, that object it best fulfilled in stepping from the known because proximate, gradually onward to the point where all certitude becomes lost in the remote. For my present purpose, however, that of enabling the mind to take in, as if from afar and at one glance, a distant conception of the *individual* Universe—it is clear that a descent to small from great—to the outskirts from the centre (if we could establish a centre)—to the end from the beginning (if we could fancy a

beginning) would be the preferable course, but
for the difficulty, if not impossibility, of presenting, in this course, to the unastronomical, a picture at all comprehensible in regard to such considerations as are involved in *quantity*—that is
to say, in number, magnitude and distance.

Now, distinctness—intelligibility, at all points,
is a primary feature in my general design. On
important topics it is better to be a good deal pro-
lix than even a very little obscure. But abstruse-
ness is a quality appertaining to no subject *per
se*. All are alike, in facility of comprehension, to
him who approaches them by properly graduated
steps. It is merely because a stepping-stone, here
and there, is heedlessly left unsupplied in our
road to Differential Calculus, that this latter is
not altogether as simple a thing as a sonnet by
Mr. Solomon Seesaw.

By way of admitting, then, no *chance* for mis-
apprehension, I think it advisable to proceed as
if even the more obvious facts of Astronomy
were unknown to the reader. In combining the
two modes of discussion to which I have referred,
I propose to avail myself of the advantages peculiar to each—and very especially of the *iteration
in detail* which will be unavoidable as a consequence of the plan. Commencing with a descent,
I shall reserve for the return upwards those in-
dispensable considerations of *quantity* to which
allusion has already been made.

Let us begin, then, at once, with that merest of
words, "Infinity." This, like "God," "spirit,"
and some other expressions of which the equiva-

lents exist in all languages, is by no means the expression of an idea, but of an effort at one. It stands for the possible attempt at an impossible conception. Man needed a term by which to point out the *direction* of this effort—the cloud behind which lay, forever invisible, the *object* of this attempt. A word, in fine, was demanded, by means of which one human being might put himself in relation at once with another human being and with a certain *tendency* of the human intellect. Out of this demand arose the word, "Infinity;" which is thus the representative but of the *thought of a thought.*

As regards *that* infinity now considered—the infinity of space—we often hear it said that "its idea is admitted by the mind—is acquiesced in—is entertained—on account of the greater difficulty which attends the conception of a limit." But this is merely one of those *phrases* by which even profound thinkers, time out of mind, have occasionally taken pleasure in deceiving *themselves.*

The quibble lies concealed in the word "difficulty." "The mind," we are told, "entertains the idea of *limitless,* through the greater *difficulty* which it finds in entertaining that of *limited,* space." Now, were the proposition but fairly *put,* its absurdity would become transparent at once. Clearly, there is no mere *difficulty* in the case. The assertion intended, if presented *according* to its intention, and without sophistry, would run thus:—"The mind admits the idea of limitless, through the greater *impossibility* of entertaining that of limited space."

It must be immediately seen that this is not a
question of two statements between whose respective credibilities—or of two arguments between
whose respective validities—the *reason* is called
upon to decide: it is a matter of two conceptions,
directly conflicting, and each avowedly impossible, one of which the *intellect* is supposed to be
capable of entertaining, on account of the greater
impossibility of entertaining the other.   The
choice is *not* made between two difficulties; it
is merely *fancied* to be made between two impossibilities.   Now of the former, there *are* degrees,
but of the latter, none:—just as our impertinent
letter-writer has already suggested.   A task *may*
be more or less difficult; but it is either possible
or not possible—there are no gradations.   It
might be more *difficult* to overthrow the Andes
than an ant-hill; but it *can* be no more *impossible* to annihilate the matter of the one than
the matter of the other.   A man may jump ten
feet with less *difficulty* than he can jump twenty,
but the *impossibility* of his leaping to the moon
is not a whit less than that of his leaping to the
dog-star.

Since all this is undeniable: since the choice of
the mind is to be made between *impossibilities*
of conception: since one impossibility cannot be
greater than another: and since, thus, one cannot be preferred to another: the philosophers
who not only maintain, on the grounds mentioned, man's *idea* of infinity but, on account of
such suppositious idea, *infinity itself*—are plainly engaged in demonstrating one impossible

thing to be possible by showing how it is that
some one other thing—is impossible too. This,
it will be said, is nonsense, and perhaps it is;
indeed I think it very capital nonsense, but fore-
go all claim to it as nonsense of mine.

The readiest mode, however, of displaying the
fallacy of the philosophical argument on this
question, is by simply adverting to a *fact* respecting it which has been hitherto quite over-
looked—the fact that the argument alluded to
both proves and disproves its own proposition.
"The mind is impelled," say the theologians and
others, "to admit a *First Cause*, by the superior
difficulty it experiences in conceiving cause beyond cause without end." The quibble, as before, lies in the word "difficulty," but *here* what
is it employed to sustain? A First Cause. And
what is a First Cause? An ultimate termination of causes? And what is an ultimate termination of causes? Finity—the Finite. Thus the
one quibble, in two processes, by God knows how
many philosophers, is made to support now Finity and now Infinity: could it not be brought to
support something besides? As for the quibbles,
they, at least, are insupportable. But, to dis-
miss them; what they prove in the one case is
the identical nothing which they demonstrate in
the other.

Of course, no one will suppose that I here con-
tend for the absolute impossibility of *that* which
we attempt to convey in the word "Infinity."
My purpose is but to show the folly of endeavoring to prove Infinity itself, or even our concep-

tion of it, by any such blundering ratiocination
as that which is ordinarily employed.

Nevertheless, as an individual, I may be permitted to say that I *cannot* conceive Infinity, and
am convinced that no human being can. A mind
not thoroughly self-conscious, not accustomed to
the introspective analysis of its own operations,
will, it is true, often deceive itself by supposing
that it *has* entertained the conception of which
we speak. In the effort to entertain it, we proceed step beyond step, we fancy point still beyond point; and so long as we *continue* the effort, it may be said, in fact, that we are *tending*
to the formation of the idea designed; while the
strength of the impression that we actually form
or have formed, is in the ratio of the period during which we keep up the mental endeavor. But
it is in the act of discontinuing the endeavor—
or fulfilling (as we think) the idea—of putting
the finishing stroke (as we suppose) to the conception—that we overthrow at once the whole
fabric of our fancy by resting upon some one
ultimate, and, therefore, definite point. This
fact, however, we fail to perceive, on account of
the absolute coincidence, in time, between the settling down upon the ultimate point and the act
of cessation in thinking. In attempting, on the
other hand, to frame the idea of a *limited* space,
we merely converse the processes which involve
the impossibility.

We *believe* in a God. We may or may not *believe* in finite or in infinite space; but our belief,
in such cases, is more properly designated as

faith, and is a matter quite distinct from that belief proper—from that *intellectual* belief—which presupposes the mental conception.

The fact is, that, upon the enunciation of any one of that class of terms to which "Infinity" belongs—the class representing *thoughts of thought*—he who has a right to say that he thinks *at all,* feels himself called upon, *not* to entertain a conception, but simply to direct his mental vision toward some given point, in the intellectual firmament, where lies a nebula never to be resolved. To solve it, indeed, he makes no effort; for with a rapid instinct he comprehends, not only the impossibility, but, as regards all human purposes, the *inessentiality* of its solution. He perceives that the Deity has not *designed* it to be solved. He sees, at once, that it lies *out* of the brain of man, and even *how,* if not exactly *why,* it lies out of it. There *are* people, I am aware, who, busying themselves in attempts at the unattainable, acquire very easily, by dint of the jargon they emit, among those thinkers-that-they-think with whom darkness and depth are synonymous, a kind of cuttle-fish reputation for profundity; but the finest quality of Thought is its self-cognizance; and with some little equivocation, it may be said that no fog of the mind can well be greater than that which, extending to the very boundaries of the mental domain, shuts out even these boundaries themselves from comprehension.

It will now be understood that, in using the phrase, "Infinity of Space," I make no call upon the reader to entertain the impossible conception of an *absolute* infinity. I refer simply to the *"utmost conceivable expanse"* of space—a shadowy and fluctuating domain, now shrinking, now swelling, in accordance with the vacillating energies of the imagination.

Hitherto, the Universe of stars has always been considered as coincident with the Universe proper, as I have defined it in the commencement of this Discourse. It has been always either directly or indirectly assumed—at least since the dawn of intelligible Astronomy—that, were it possible for us to attain any given point in space, we should still find, on all sides of us, an interminable succession of stars. This was the untenable idea of Pascal when making perhaps the most successful attempt ever made, at periphrasing the conception for which we struggle in the word "Universe." "It is a sphere," he says, "of which the centre is everywhere, the circumference, nowhere." But although this intended definition is, in fact, *no* definition of the Universe of *stars,* we may accept it, with some mental reservation, as a definition (rigorous enough for all practical purposes) of the Universe *proper*—that is to say, of the Universe of *space.* This latter, then, let us regard as *"a sphere of which the centre is everywhere, the circumference nowhere."* In fact, while we find it impossible to fancy an *end* to space, we have no difficulty. in picturing to ourselves any one of an infinity of *beginnings*.

As our starting point, then, let us adopt the

Godhead. Of this Godhead, *in itself,* he alone is not imbecile—he alone is not impious who propounds——nothing. *"Nous ne connaissons rien,"* says the Baron de Bielfeld—*"Nous ne connaissons rien de la nature ou de l'essence de Dieu:—pour savior ce qu'il est, il faut être Dieu même."*—"We know absolutely *nothing* of the nature or essence of God:—in order to comprehend what He is, we should have to be God ourselves."

"We should have to be God ourselves!"—With a phrase so startling as this yet ringing in my ears, I nevertheless venture to demand if this our present ignorance of the Deity is an ignorance to which the soul is *everlastingly* condemned.

By *Him,* however—*now,* at least, the Incomprehensible—by Him—assuming him as *Spirit*—that is to say, as *not Matter*—a distinction which, for all intelligible purposes, will stand well instead of a definition—by Him, then, existing as Spirit, let us content ourselves, to-night, with supposing to have been *created,* or made out of Nothing, by dint of his Volition—at some point of Space which we will take as the centre—at some period into which we do not pretend to inquire, but at all events immensely remote—by Him, then again, let us suppose to have been created——*what?* This is a vitally momentous epoch in our considerations. *What* is it that we are justified—that alone we are justified in supposing to have been, primarily and solely, created?

We have attained a point where only *Intuition* can aid us:—but new let me recur to the idea which I have already suggested as that alone which we can properly entertain of intuition. It is but *the conviction arising from those inductions or deductions of which the processes are so shadowy as to escape our consciousness, elude our reason, or defy our capacity of expression.* With this understanding, I now assert—that an intuition altogether irresistible, although inexpressible, forces me to the conclusion that what God originally created—that that Matter which, by dint of his Volition, he first made from his Spirit, or from Nihility, *could* have been nothing but Matter in its utmost conceivable state of—— what?—of *Simplicity?*

This will be found the sole absolute *assumption* of my Discourse. I use the word "assumption" in its ordinary sense; yet I maintain that even this my primary proposition, is very, very far indeed, from being really a mere assumption. Nothing was ever more certainly—no human conclusion was ever, in fact, more regularly—more rigorously *deduced*:—but, alas! the processes lie out of the human analysis—at all events are beyond the utterance of the human tongue.

Let us now endeavor to conceive what Matter must be, when, or if, in its absolute extreme of *Simplicity.* Here the Reason flies at once to Imparticularity—to a particle—to *one* particle—a particle of *one* kind—of *one* character—of *one* nature—of *one size*—of one form—a particle, therefore, *"without* form and void"—a particle positively a particle at all points—a particle absolutely unique, individual, undivided, and not indivisible only because He who *created* it, by dint of his Will, can by an infinitely less energetic exercise of the same Will, as a matter of course, divide it.

Oneness, then, is all that I predicate of the originally created Matter; but I propose to show that this *Oneness is a principle abundantly sufficient to account for the constitution, the existing phœnomena and the plainly inevitable annihilation of at least the material Universe.*

The willing into being the primordial particle, has completed the act, or more properly the *conception* of Creation. We now proceed to the ultimate purpose for which we are to suppose the Particle created—that is to say, the ultimate purpose so far as our considerations *yet* enable us to see it—the constitution of the Universe from it, the Particle.

This constitution has been effected by *forcing* the originally and therefore normally *One* into the abnormal condition of *Many.* An action of this character implies reaction. A diffusion from Unity, under the conditions, involves a tendency to return into Unity—a tendency ineradicable until satisfied. But on these points I will speak more fully hereafter.

The assumption of absolute Unity in the primordial Particle includes that of infinite divisibility. Let us conceive the Particle, then, to be only not totally exhausted by diffusion into Space. From the one Particle, as a centre, let us suppose to be irradiated spherically—in all directions—to immeasurable but still definite distances in the previously vacant space—a certain inexpressibly great yet limited number of unimaginably yet not infinitely minute atoms.

Now, of these atoms, thus diffused, or upon diffusion, what conditions are we permitted—not to assume, but to infer, from consideration as well of their source as of the character of the design apparent in their diffusion? *Unity* being their source, and *difference from Unity* the character of the design manifested in their diffusion, we are warranted in supposing this character to be at least *generally* preserved throughout the design, and to form a portion of the design itself: —that is to say, we shall be warranted in conceiving continual differences at all points from the uniquity and simplicity of the origin. But, for these reasons, shall we be justified in imagining the atoms heterogeneous, dissimilar, unequal, and inequidistant? More explicitly—are we to consider no two atoms as, at their diffusion, of the same nature, or of the same form, or of the same size?—and, after fulfilment of their diffusion into Space, is absolute inequidistance, each from each, to be understood of all of them? In such arrangement, under such conditions, we most easily and immediately comprehend the subsequent most feasible carrying out to completion of any such design as that which I have suggested—the design of variety out of unity—diversity out of sameness—heterogeneity out of homogeneity—complexity out of simplicity—in a word, the utmost possible multiplicity of *relation* out of the emphatically irrelative *One*. Undoubtedly, therefore, we *should* be warranted in assuming all that has been mentioned, but for the reflection, first, that supererogation is not presumable of any Divine Act; and, secondly, that the object supposed in view, appears as feasible when some of the conditions in question are dispensed with, in the beginning, as when all are understood immediately to exist. I mean to say that some are involved in the rest, or so instantaneous a consequence of them as to make the distinction inappreciable. Difference of *size,* for example, will at once be brought about through the tendency of one atom to a second, in preference to a third, on account of particular inequidistance; which is to be comprehended as *particular inequidistances between centres of quantity, in neighboring atoms of different form*—a matter not at all interfering with the generally-equable distribution of the atoms. Difference of *kind,* too, is easily conceived to be merely a result of differences in size and form, taken more or less conjointly:—in fact, since the *Unity* of the Particle Proper implies absolute homogeneity, we cannot imagine the atoms, at their diffusion, differing in kind, without imagining, at the same time, a special exercise of the Divine Will, at the emission of each atom, for the purpose of effecting, in each, a change of its essential nature:—so fantastic an idea is the less to be indulged, as the object proposed is seen to be thoroughly attainable without such minute and elaborate in-

IX. 3

terposition. We perceive, therefore, upon the whole, that it would be supererogatory, and consequently unphilosophical, to predicate of the atoms, in view of their purposes, any thing more than *difference of form* at their dispersion, with particular inequidistance after it—all other differences arising at once out of these, in the very first processes of mass-constitution:—We thus establish the Universe on a purely *geometrical* basis. Of course, it is by no means necessary to assume absolute difference, even of form, among *all* the atoms irradiated—any more than absolute particular inequidistance of each from each. We are required to conceive merely that no *neighboring* atoms are of similar form—no atoms which can ever approximate, until their inevitable reunition at the end.

Although the immediate and perpetual *tendency* of the disunited atoms to return into their normal Unity, is implied, as I have said, in their abnormal diffusion, still it is clear that this tendency will be without consequence—a tendency and no more—until the diffusive energy, in ceasing to be exerted, shall leave *it*, the tendency, free to seek its satisfaction. The Divine Act, however, being considered as determinate, and discontinued on fulfilment of the diffusion, we understand, at once, a *reaction*—in other words, a *satisfiable* tendency of the disunited atoms to return into *One*.

But the diffusive energy being withdrawn, and the reaction having commenced in furtherance of the ultimate design—*that of the utmost possible*

Relation—this design is now in danger of being
frustrated, in detail, by reason of that very tendency to return which is to effect its accomplish-
ment in general. *Multiplicity* is the object; but
there is nothing to prevent proximate atoms from
lapsing *at once,* through the now satisfiable tendency—*before* the fulfilment of any ends proposed in multiplicity—into absolute oneness
among themselves:—there is nothing to impede
the aggregation of various *unique* masses, at various points of space:—in other words, nothing
to interfere with the accumulation of various
masses, each absolutely One.

For the effectual and thorough completion of
the general design, we thus see the necessity for
a repulsion of limited capacity—a separative
something which, on withdrawal of the diffusive
Volition, shall at the same time allow the approach, and forbid the junction, of the atoms;
suffering them infinitely to approximate, while
denying them positive contact; in a word, having
the power—*up to a certain epoch*—of preventing
their *coalition,* but no ability to interfere with
their *coalescence* in any respect or *degree.* The
repulsion, already considered as so peculiarly
limited in other regards, must be understood, let
me repeat, as having power to prevent absolute
coalition, *only up to a certain epoch.* Unless we
are to conceive that the appetite for Unity among
the atoms is doomed to be satisfied *never;*—unless we are to conceive that what had a beginning
is to have an end—a conception which cannot
really be entertained, however much we may talk

or dream of entertaining it—we are forced to conclude that the repulsive influence imagined, will, finally—under pressure of the *Uni-tendency collectively* applied, but never and in no degree *until*, on fulfilment of the Divine purposes, such collective application shall be naturally made— yield to a force which, at that ultimate epoch, shall be the superior force precisely to the extent required, and thus permit the universal subsidence into the inevitable, because original and therefore normal, *One.* The conditions here to be reconciled are difficult indeed:—we cannot even comprehend the possibility of their conciliation;—nevertheless, the apparent impossibility is brilliantly suggestive.

That the repulsive something actually exists, *we see.* Man neither employs, nor knows, a force sufficient to bring two atoms into contact. This is but the well-established proposition of the impenetrability of matter. All Experiment proves —all Philosophy admits it. The *design* of the repulsion—the necessity for its existence—I have endeavored to show; but from all attempt at investigating its nature have religiously abstained; this on account of an intuitive conviction that the principle at issue is strictly spiritual—lies in a recess impervious to our present understanding—lies involved in a consideration of what now —in our human state—is *not* to be considered— in a consideration of *Spirit in itself.* I feel, in a word, that here the God has interposed, and here only, because here and here only the knot demanded the interposition of the God.

In fact, while the tendency of the diffused atoms to return into Unity, will be recognised, at once, as the principle of the Newtonian Gravity, what I have spoken of as a repulsive influence prescribing limits to the (immediate) satisfaction of the tendency, will be understood as *that* which we have been in the practice of designating now as heat, now as magnetism, now as *electricity;* displaying our ignorance of its awful character in the vacillation of the phraseology with which we endeavor to circumscribe it.

Calling it, merely for the moment, electricity, we know that all experimental analysis of electricity has given, as an ultimate result, the principle, or seeming principle, *heterogeneity. Only* where things differ, is electricity apparent; and it is presumable that they *never* differ where it is not developed at least, if not apparent. Now, this result is in the fullest keeping with that which I have reached unempirically. The design of the repulsive influence I have maintained to be that of preventing immediate Unity among the diffused atoms; and these atoms are represented as different each from each. *Difference* is their character—their essentiality—just as *no-difference* was the essentiality of their course. When we say, then, that an attempt to bring any two of these atoms together would induce an effort, on the part of the repulsive influence, to prevent the contact, we may as well use the strictly convertible sentence that an attempt to bring together any two differences will result in a development of electricity. All existing bodies, of

course, are composed of these atoms in proximate
contact, and are therefore to be considered as
mere assemblages of more or fewer differences;
and the resistance made by the repulsive spirit,
on bringing together any two such assemblages,
would be in the ratio of the two sums of the differences in each:—an expression which, when reduced, is equivalent to this:—*The amount of electricity developed on the approximation of two
bodies, is proportional to the difference between
the respective sums of the atoms of which the
bodies are composed.* That *no* two bodies are absolutely alike, is a simple corollary from all that
has been here said. Electricity, therefore, existing always, is *developed* whenever *any* bodies, but
manifested only when bodies of appreciable difference, are brought into approximation.

To electricity—so, for the present, continuing
to call it—we *may* not be wrong in referring the
various physical appearances of light, heat and
magnetism; but far less shall we be liable to err
in attributing to this strictly spiritual principle
the more important phænomena of vitality, consciousness and *Thought*. On this topic, however,
I need pause *here* merely to suggest that these
phænomena, whether observed generally or in
detail, seem to proceed *at least in the ratio of the
heterogeneous.*

Discarding now the two equivocal terms,
"gravitation" and "electricity," let us adopt
the more definite expressions, *"attraction"* and
"repulsion." The former is the body; the latter
the soul: the one is the material; the other the

spiritual, principle of the Universe. *No other principles exist.* *All* phænomena are referable to one, or to the other, or to both combined. So rigorously is this the case—so thoroughly demonstrable is it that attraction and repulsion are the *sole* properties through which we perceive the Universe—in other words, by which Matter is manifested to Mind—that, for all merely argumentative purposes, we are fully justified in assuming that matter *exists* only as attraction and repulsion—that attraction and repulsion *are* matter:—there being no conceivable case in which we may not employ the term "matter" and the terms "attraction" and "repulsion," taken together, as equivalent, and therefore convertible, expressions in Logic.

I said, just now, that what I have described as the tendency of the diffused atoms to return into their original unity, would be understood as the principle of the Newtonian law of gravity; and, in fact, there can be but little difficulty in such an understanding, if we look at the Newtonian gravity in a merely general view, as a force impelling matter to seek matter; that is to say, when we pay no attention to the known *modus operandi* of the Newtonian force. The general coincidence satisfies us; but, upon looking closely, we see, in detail, much that appears *in*coincident, and much in regard to which no coincidence, at least, is established. For example: the Newtonian gravity, when we think of it in certain moods, does *not* seem to be a tendency to *oneness* at all, but rather a tendency of all bodies in all direc-

tions—a phrase apparently expressive of a tendency to diffusion. Here, then, is an *incoinci-
dence*. Again; when we reflect on the mathematical *law* governing the Newtonian tendency, we
see clearly that no coincidence has been made
good, in respect of the *modus operandi*, at least,
between gravitation as known to exist and that
seemingly simple and direct tendency which I
have assumed.

In fact, I have attained a point at which it will
be advisable to strengthen my position by re-
versing my processes. So far, we have gone on
a priori, from an abstract consideration of *Simplicity*, as that quality most likely to have characterized the original action of God. Let us now
see whether the established facts of the Newtonian Gravitation may not afford us, *a posteriori*,
some legitimate inductions.

What does the Newtonian law declare? That
all bodies attract each other with forces proportional to the squares of their distances. Pur-
posely, I have given, in the first place, the vulgar
version of the law; and I confess that in this, as
in most other vulgar versions of great truths, we
find little of a suggestive character. Let us now
adopt a more philosophical phraseology:—*Every
atom, of every body, attracts every other atom,
both of its own and of every other body, with a
force which varies inversely as the squares of the
distances between the attracting and attracted
atom.* Here, indeed, a flood of suggestion bursts
upon the mind.

But let us see distinctly what it was that New-

ton *proved*—according to the grossly irrational
definitions of *proof* prescribed by the metaphysical schools. He was forced to content himself
with showing how thoroughly the motions of an
imaginary Universe, composed of attracting and
attracted atoms obedient to the law he an-
nounced, coincide with those of the actually existing Universe so far as it comes under our observation. This was the amount of his *demonstration*—that is to say, this was the amount of
it, according to the conventional cant of the
"philosophies." His successes added proof mul-
tiplied by proof—such proof as a sound intellect admits—but the *demonstration* of the law
itself, persist the metaphysicians, had not been
strengthened in any degree. "*Ocular, physical*
proof," however, of attraction, here upon Earth,
in accordance with the Newtonian theory, was,
at length, much to the satisfaction of some intellectual grovellers, afforded. This proof arose col-
laterally and incidentally (as nearly all important truths have arisen) out of an attempt to ascertain the mean density of the Earth. In the
famous Maskelyne, Cavendish and Bailly experiments for this purpose, the attraction of the mass
of a mountain was seen, felt, measured, and
found to be mathematically consistent with the
immortal theory of the British astronomer.

But in spite of this confirmation of that which
needed none—in spite of the so-called corroboration of the "theory" by the so-called "ocular
and physical proof"—in spite of the *character* of
this corroboration—the ideas which even really

philosophical men cannot help imbibing of gravity—and, especially, the ideas of it which ordinary men get and contentedly maintain, are *seen*
to have been derived, for the most part, from a
consideration of the principle as they find it developed—*merely in the planet upon which they
stand.*

Now, to what does so partial a consideration
tend—to what species of error does it give rise?
On the Earth we *see* and *feel* only that gravity
impels all bodies towards the *centre* of the Earth.
No man in the common walks of life could be
made to see or feel anything else—could be made
to perceive that anything, anywhere, has a perpetual, gravitating tendency in any *other* direction than to the centre of the Earth; yet (with
an exception hereafter to be specified) it is a fact
that every earthly thing (not to speak now of
every heavenly thing) has a tendency not *only*
to the Earth's centre but in every conceivable
direction besides.

Now, although the philosophic cannot be said
to *err with* the vulgar in this matter, they nevertheless permit themselves to be influenced, without knowing it, by the *sentiment* of the vulgar
idea. "Although the Pagan fables are not believed," says Bryant, in his very erudite "Myth-
ology," yet we forget ourselves continually and
make inferences from them as from existing realities." I mean to assert that the merely *sensitive perception* of gravity as we experience it on
Earth, beguiles mankind into the fancy of *concentralization* or *especiality* respecting it—has

been continually biasing towards this fancy even
the mightiest intellects—perpetually, although
imperceptibly, leading them away from the real
characteristics of the principle; thus preventing
them, up to this date, from ever getting a glimpse
of that vital truth which lies in a diametrically
opposite direction—behind the principle's *essential* characteristics—those, *not* of concentralization or especiality—but of *universality* and *diffusion*. This "vital truth" is *Unity* as the *source*
of the phænomenon.

Let me now repeat the definition of gravity:—
*Every atom, of every body, attracts every other
atom, both of its own and of every other body,*
with a force which varies inversely as the squares
of the distances of the attracting and attracted
atom.

Here let the reader pause with me, for a moment, in contemplation of the miraculous—of the
ineffable—of the altogether unimaginable complexity of relation involved in the fact that *each
atom attracts every other atom*—involved merely
in this fact of the attraction, without reference
to the law or mode in which the attraction is
manifested—involved *merely* in the fact that
each atom attracts every other atom *at all,* in a
wilderness of atoms so numerous that those which
go to the composition of a cannon-ball, exceed,
probably, in mere point of number, all the stars
which go to the constitution of the Universe.

Had we discovered, simply, that each atom
tended to some one favorite point—to some especially attractive atom—we should still have

fallen upon a discovery which, in itself, would have sufficed to overwhelm the mind:—but what is it that we are actually called upon to comprehend? That each atom attracts—sympathizes with the most delicate movements of every other atom, and with each and with all at the same time, and forever, and according to a determinate law of which the complexity, even considered by itself solely, is utterly beyond the grasp of the imagination of man. If I propose to ascertain the influence of one mote in a sunbeam upon its neighboring mote, I cannot accomplish my purpose without first counting and weighing all the atoms in the Universe, and defining the precise positions of all at one particular moment. If I venture to displace, by even the billionth part of an inch, the microscopical speck of dust which lies now upon the point of my finger, what is the character of that act upon which I have adventured? I have done a deed which shakes the Moon in her path, which causes the Sun to be no longer the sun, and which alters forever the destiny of the multitudinous myriads of stars that roll and glow in the majestic presence of their Creator.

These ideas—conceptions such as *these*—unthoughtlike thoughts—soul-reveries rather than conclusions or even considerations of the intellect:—ideas, I repeat, such as these, are such as we can alone hope profitably to entertain in any effort at grasping the great principle, *Attraction*.

But now, *with* such ideas—with such a *vision* of the marvellous complexity of Attraction fairly in his mind—let any person competent of thought on such topics as these, set himself to the task of imagining a *principle* for the phænomena observed—a condition from which they sprang.

Does not so evident a brotherhood among the atoms point to a common parentage? Does not a sympathy so omniprevalent, so ineradicable, and so thoroughly irrespective, suggest a common paternity as its source? Does not one extreme impel the reason to the other? Does not the infinitude of division refer to the utterness of individuality? Does not the entireness of the complex hint at the perfection of the simple? It is *not* that the atoms, as we see them, are divided or that they are complex in their relations—but that they are inconceivably divided and unutterably complex: it is the extremeness of the conditions to which I now allude, rather than to the conditions themselves. In a word, is it not because the atoms were, at some remote epoch of time, even *more than together*—is it not because originally, and therefore normally, they were *One*—that now, in all circumstances—at all points—in all directions—by all modes of approach—in all relations and through all conditions—they struggle *back* to this absolutely, this irrelatively, this unconditionally *one?*

Some person may here demand:—"Why—since it is to the *One* that the atoms struggle back —do we not find and define Attraction 'a merely general tendency to a centre?'—why, in especial, do not *your* atoms—the atoms which you describe as having been irradiated from a centre—proceed at once, rectilinearly, back to the central point of their origin?''

I reply that *they do;* as will be distinctly shown; but that the cause of their so doing is quite irrespective of the centre *as such*. They all tend rectilinearly towards a centre, because of the sphericity with which they have been irradiated into space. Each atom, forming one of a generally uniform globe of atoms, finds more atoms in the direction of the centre, of course, than in any other, and in that direction, therefore, is impelled—but is *not* thus impelled because the centre is *the point of its origin*. It is not to any *point* that the atoms are allied. It is not any *locality*, either in the concrete or in the abstract, to which I suppose them bound. Nothing like *location* was conceived as their origin. Their source lies in the principle, *Unity*. *This* is their lost parent. *This* they seek always—immediately—in all directions—wherever it is even partially to be found; thus appeasing, in some measure, the ineradicable tendency, while on the way to its absolute satisfaction in the end. It follows from all this, that any principle which shall be adequate to account for the *law*, or *modus operandi*, of the attractive force in general, will account for this law in particular:—that is to say, any principle which will show why the atoms should tend to their *general centre of irradiation* with forces inversely proportional to the squares of the distances will be admitted as satisfactorily accounting, at the same time, for the tendency, according to the same law, of these atoms each to each;—*for* the tendency to the centre *is* merely the tendency each to each, and not any tendency to a centre as such.—Thus it will be seen, also, that the establishment of my propositions would involve no *necessity* of modification in the terms of the Newtonian definition of Gravity, which declares that each atom attracts each other atom and so forth, and declares this merely; but (always under the supposition that what I propose be, in the end, admitted) it seems clear that some error might occasionally be avoided, in the future processes of Science, were a more ample phraseology adopted:—for instance:—"Each atom tends to every other atom, &c., with a force &c.: *the general result being a tendency of all, with a similar force, to a general centre.*"

The reversal of our processes has thus brought us to an identical result; but while in the one process *intuition* was the starting point, in the other it was the goal. In commencing the former journey I could only say that, with an irresistible intuition, I *felt* Simplicity to have been made the characteristic of the original action of God:—in ending the letter I can only declare that with an irresistible intuition, I perceive Unity to have been the source of the observed phænomena of the Newtonian gravitation. Thus, according to the schools, I *prove* nothing. So be it:—I design but to suggest—and to *convince* through the suggestion. I am proudly aware that there exist many of the most profound and cautiously discriminative human intellects which

cannot *help* being abundantly content with my—
suggestions. To these intellects—as to my own
—there is no mathematical demonstration which
could bring the least additional *true proof* of the
great *Truth* which I have advanced—*the truth of
Original Unity as the source—as the principle of
the Universal Phœnomena*. For my part I am not
sure that I speak and see—I am not so sure that
my heart beats and that my soul lives:—of the
rising of to-morrow's sun—a probability that as
yet lies in the Future—I do not pretend to be one
thousandth part as sure—as I am of the irretrievably bygone *Fact* that All Things and All
Thoughts of Things, with all their ineffable Multiplicity of Relation, sprang at once into being
from the primordial and irrelative *One*.

Referring to the Newtonian Gravity, Dr.
Nichol, the eloquent author of "The Architecture of the Heavens," says:—"In truth we have
no reason to suppose this great Law, as now revealed, to be the ultimate or simplest, and there-
for the universal and all-comprehensive, form of
a great Ordinance. The mode in which its in-
tensity diminishes with the element of distance,
has not the aspect of an ultimate *principle;*
which always assumes the simplicity and self-
evidence of those axioms which constitute the
basis of Geometry."

Now, it is quite true that "ultimate principles," in the common understanding of the
words, always assume the simplicity of geometrical axioms—(as for "self-evidence," there is no
such thing)—but these principles are clearly *not*

"ultimate;" in other terms, what we are in the habit of calling principles are no principles, properly speaking—since there can be but one *principle*, the Volition of God. We have no right to assume, then, from what we observe in rules that we choose foolishly to name "principles," anything at all in respect to the characteristics of a principle proper. The "ultimate principles" of which Dr. Nichol speaks as having geometrical simplicity, may and do have this geometrical turn, as being part and parcel of a vast geometrical system, and thus a system of simplicity itself—in which, nevertheless, the *truly* ultimate principle is, *as we know,* the consummation of the complex—that is to say, of the unintelligible—for is it not the Spiritual Capacity of God?

I quoted Dr. Nichol's remark, however, not so much to question its philosophy, as by way of calling attention to the fact that while all men have admitted *some* principle as existing behind the law of Gravity, no attempt has been yet made to point out what this principle in particular *is:*—if we except, perhaps, occasional fantastic efforts at referring it to Magnetism, or Mesmerism, or Swedenborgianism, or Transcendentalism, or some other equally delicious *ism* of the same species, and invariably patronized by one and the same species of people. The great mind of Newton, while boldly grasping the Law itself, shrank from the principle of the Law. The more fluent and comprehensive at least, if not the more patient and profound, sagacity of La-

IX. 4

place, had not the courage to attack it. But hesitation on the part of these two astronomers it is, perhaps, not so very difficult to understand. They, as well as all the first class of mathematicians, were mathematicians *solely:*—their intellect at least had a firmly-pronounced mathematico-physical tone. What lay not distinctly within the domain of Physics, or of Mathematics, seemed to them either Non-Entity or Shadow. Nevertheless, we may well wonder that Leibnitz, who was a marked exception to the general rule in these respects, and whose mental temperament was a singular admixture of the mathematical with the physico-metaphysical, did not at once investigate and establish the point at issue. Either Newton or Laplace, seeking a principle and discovering none *physical,* would have rested contentedly in the conclusion that there was absolutely none; but it is almost impossible to fancy, of Leibnitz, that, having exhausted in his search the physical dominions, he would not have stepped at once, boldly and hopefully, amid his old familiar haunts in the kingdom of Metaphysics. Here, indeed, it is clear that he *must* have adventured in search of the treasure:— that he did not find it after all, was, perhaps, because his fairy guide, Imagination, was not sufficiently well-grown, or well-educated, to direct him aright.

I observed, just now, that, in fact, there had been certain vague attempts at referring Gravity to some very uncertain *isms.* These attempts, however, although considered bold, and justly so

considered, looked no farther than to the generality—the merest generality—of the Newtonian Law. Its *modus operandi* has never, to my
knowledge, been approached in the way of an effort at explanation. It is therefore, with no unwarranted fear of being taken for a madman at
the outset, and before I can bring my propositions fairly to the eye of those who alone are
competent to decide upon them, that I here declare the *modus operandi* of the Law of Gravity
to be an exceedingly simple and perfectly explicable thing—that is to say, when we make our
advances towards it in just gradations and in
the true direction—when we regard it from the
proper point of view.

Whether we reach the idea of absolute *Unity*
as the source of All Things, from a consideration
of Simplicity as the most probable characteristic
of the original action of God;—whether we arrive at it from an inspection of the universality
of relation in the gravitating phænomena;—or
whether we attain it as a result of the mutual
corroboration afforded by both processes;—still,
the idea itself, if entertained at all, is entertained in inseparable connection with another
idea—that of the condition of the Universe of
stars as we *now* perceive it—that is to say, a
condition of immeasurable *diffusion* through
space. Now a connection between these two
ideas—unity and diffusion—cannot be established unless through the entertainment of a
third idea—that of *irradiation*. Absolute Unity
being taken as a centre, then the existing Uni-

verse of stars is the result of *irradiation* from
that centre.

Now, the laws of irradiation are *known*. They
are part and parcel of the *sphere*. They belong
to the class of *indisputable geometrical properties*. We say of them, "they are true—they are
evident." To demand *why* they are true, would
be to demand why the axioms are true upon
which their demonstration is based. *Nothing* is
demonstrable, strictly speaking; but *if* anything
be, then the properties—the laws in question are
demonstrated.

But these laws—what do they declare? Irradiation—how—by what steps does it proceed outwardly from a centre?

From a *luminous* centre, *Light* issues by irradiation; and the quantities of light received upon
any given plane, supposed to be shifting its position so as to be now nearer the centre and now
farther from it, will be diminished in the same
proportion as the squares of the distances of the
plane from the luminous body, are increased;
and will be increased in the same proportion as
these squares are diminished.

The expression of the law may be thus gen-
eralized:—the number of light-particles (or, if
the phrase be preferred, the number of light-
impressions) received upon the shifting plane,
will be *inversely* proportional with the squares
of the distances of the plane. Generalizing yet
again, we may say that the diffusion—the scat-
tering—the irradiation, in a word—is *directly*
proportional with the squares of the distances.

For example: at the distance B, from the luminous centre A, a certain number of particles are so diffused as to occupy the surface B. Then at

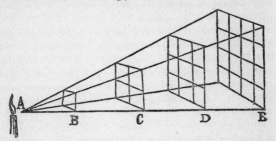

double the distance—that is to say, at C—they will be so much farther diffused as to occupy four such surfaces:—at treble the distance, or at D, they will be so much farther separated as to occupy nine such surfaces;—while, at quadruple the distance, or at E, they will have become so scattered as to spread themselves over sixteen such surfaces—and so on forever.

In saying, generally, that the irradiation proceeds in direct proportion with the squares of the distances, we use the term irradiation to express *the degree of the diffusion* as we proceed outwardly from the centre. Conversing the idea, and employing the word "concentralization," to express *the degree of the drawing together* as we come back toward the centre from an outward position, we may say that concentralization proceeds *inversely* as the squares of the distances. In other words, we have reached

the conclusion that, on the hypothesis that matter was originally irradiated from a centre, and
is now returning to it, the concentralization, in
the return, proceeds *exactly as we know the force
of gravitation to proceed.*

Now here, if we could be permitted to assume
that concentralization exactly represented the
force of the tendency to the centre—that the one
was exactly proportional to the other, and that
the two proceeded together—we should have
shown all that is required. The sole difficulty
existing, then, is to establish a direct proportion
between ''concentralization'' and the *force* of
concentralization; and this is done, of course, if
we establish such proportion between ''irradiation'' and the *force* of irradiation.

A very slight inspection of the Heavens assures us that the stars have a certain general uniformity, equability, or equidistance, of distribution through that region of space in which, collectively, and in a roughly globular form, they are
situated:—this species of very general, rather
than absolute, equability, being in full keeping
with my deduction of inequidistance, within certain limits, among the originally diffused atoms,
as a corollary from the evident design of infinite
complexity of relation out of irrelation. I
started, it will be remembered, with the idea of
a generally uniform but particularly *un*uniform
distribution of the atoms;—an idea, I repeat,
which an inspection of the stars, as they exist,
confirms.

But even in the merely general equability of

distribution, as regards the atoms, there appears a difficulty which, no doubt, has already suggested itself to those among my readers who have borne in mind that I suppose this equability of distribution effected through *irradiation from a centre*. The very first glance at the idea, irradiation, forces us to the entertainment of the hitherto unseparated and seemingly inseparable idea of agglomeration about a centre, with dispersion as we recede from it—the idea, in a word, of *in*equability of distribution in respect to the matter irradiated.

Now, I have elsewhere* observed, that it is by just such difficulties as the one now in question—such roughnesses—such peculiarities—such protuberances above the plane of the ordinary—that Reason feels her way, if at all, in her search for the True. By the difficulty—the "peculiarity"—now presented, I leap at once to *the* secret—a secret which I might never have attained *but* for the peculiarity and the inferences which, *in its mere character of peculiarity*, it affords me.

The process of thought, at this point, may be thus roughly sketched:—I say to myself—"Unity, as I have explained it, is a truth—I feel it. Diffusion is a truth—I see it. Irradiation, by which alone these two truths are reconciled, is a consequent truth—I perceive it. *Equability* or diffusion, first deduced *a priori* and then corroborated by the inspection of phænomena, is also a truth—I fully admit it. So far all

* " Murders in the Rue Morgue "—vol. IV., present edition.

is clear around me:—there are no clouds behind which *the* secret—the great secret of the gravitating *modus operandi*—can possibly lie hidden; —but this secret lies *hereabouts*, most assuredly; and *were* there but a cloud in view, I should be driven to suspicion of that cloud." And now, just as I say this, there actually comes a cloud into view. This cloud is the seeming impossibility of reconciling my truth, *irradiation*, with my truth, *equability of diffusion*. I say now: —"Behind this *seeming* impossibility is to be found what I desire." I do not say *"real* impossibility;" for invincible faith in my truths assures me that it is a mere difficulty after all; but I go on to say, with unflinching confidence, that, *when* this *difficulty* shall be solved, we shall find, *wrapped up in the process of solution,* the key to the secret at which we aim. Moreover— I *feel* that we shall discover *but one* possible solution of the difficulty; this for the reason that, were there two, one would be supererogatory—would be fruitless—would be empty— would contain no key—since no duplicate key can be needed to any secret of Nature.

And, now, let us see:—Our usual notions of irradiation—in fact, *all* our distinct notions of it—are caught merely from the process as we see it exemplified in *Light.* Here there is a *continuous* outpouring of *ray-streams,* and *with a force which we have at least no right to suppose varies at all.* Now, in any such irradiation *as this*—continuous and of unvarying force—the regions nearer the centre must *inevitably* be always more crowded with the irradiated matter than the regions more remote. But I have assumed *no* such irradiation *as this*. I assumed no *continuous* irradiation; and for the simple reason that such an assumption would have involved, first, the necessity of entertaining a conception which I have shown no man *can* entertain, and which (as I will more fully explain hereafter) all observation of the firmament refutes—the conception of the absolute infinity of the Universe of stars—and would have involved, secondly, the impossibility of understanding a reaction —that is, gravitation—as existing now—since, while an act is continued, no reaction, of course, can take place. My assumption, then, or rather my inevitable deduction from just premises— was that of a *determinate* irradiation—one finally *dis*continued.

Let me now describe the sole possible mode in which it is conceivable that matter could have been diffused through space, so as to fulfil the conditions at once of irradiation and of generally equable distribution.

For convenience of illustration, let us imagine, in the first place, a hollow sphere of glass, or of anything else, occupying the space throughout which the universal matter is to be thus equally diffused, by means of irradiation, from the absolute, irrelative, unconditional particle, placed in the centre of the sphere.

Now, a certain exertion of the diffusive power (presumed to be the Divine Volition)—in other words, a certain *force*—whose measure is the

quantity of matter—that is to say, the number
of atoms—emitted; emits, by irradiation, this
certain number of atoms; forcing them in all
directions outwardly from the centre—their
proximity to each other diminishing as they proceed—until, finally, they are distributed, loosely,
over the interior surface of the sphere.

When these atoms have attained this position,
or while proceeding to attain it, a second and
inferior exercise of the same force—or a second
and inferior force of the same character—emits,
in the same manner—that is to say, by irradiation
as before—a second stratum of atoms which proceeds to deposit itself upon the first; the number of atoms, in this case as in the former, being
of course the measure of the force which emitted
them; in other words, the force being precisely
adapted to the purpose it affects—the force, and
the number of atoms sent out by the force, being
directly proportional.

When this second stratum has reached its
destined position—or while approaching it—a
third still inferior exertion of the force, or a
third inferior force of a similar character—the
number of atoms emitted being in *all* cases the
measure of the force—proceeds to deposit a third
stratum upon the second:—and so on, until these
concentric strata, growing gradually less and
less, come down at length to the central point;
and the diffusive matter, simultaneously with the
diffusive force, is exhausted.

We have now the sphere filled, through means
of irradiation, with atoms equably diffused. The

two necessary conditions—those of irradiation
and of equable diffusion—are satisfied; and by
the *sole* process in which the possibility of their
simultaneous satisfaction is conceivable. For
this reason, I confidently expect to find, lurking
in the present condition of the atoms as distributed throughout the sphere, the secret of
which I am in search—the all-important principle of the *modus operandi* of the Newtonian
law. Let us examine, then, the actual condition
of the atoms.

They lie in a series of concentric strata. They
are equably diffused throughout the sphere.
They have been irradiated into these states.

The atoms being *equably* distributed, the
greater the superficial extent of any of these concentric strata, or spheres, the more atoms will
lie upon it. In other words, the number of
atoms lying upon the surface of any one of the
concentric spheres, is directly proportional with
the extent of that surface.

*But, in any series of concentric spheres, the
surfaces are directly proportional with the
squares of the distances from the centre.**

Therefore the number of atoms in any stratum
is directly proportional with the square of that
stratum's distance from the centre.

But the number of atoms in any stratum is
the measure of the force which emitted that
stratum—that is to say, is *directly proportional*
with the force.

---

* Succinctly—The surfaces of spheres are as the squares of
their radii.

Therefore the force which irradiated any stratum is directly proportional with the square of that stratum's distance from the centre:—or, generally,

The force of the irradiation has been directly proportional with the squares of the distances.

Now, Reaction, as far as we know any thing of it, is Action conversed. The *general* principle of Gravity being, in the first place, understood as the reaction of an act—as the expression of a desire on the part of Matter, while existing in a state of diffusion, to return into the Unity whence it was diffused; and, in the second place, the mind being called upon to determine the *character* of the desire—the manner in which it would, naturally, be manifested; in other words, being called upon to conceive a probable law, or *modus operandi,* for the return; could not well help arriving at the conclusion that this law of return would be precisely the converse of the law of departure. That such would be the case, any one, at least, would be abundantly justified in taking for granted, until such time as some person should suggest something like a plausible reason why it should *not* be the case—until such period as a law of return shall be imagined which the intellect can consider as preferable.

Matter, then, irradiated into space with a force varying as the squares of the distances, might *a priori,* be supposed to return towards its centre of irradiation with a force varying *inversely* as the squares of the distances: and I have already

shown* that any principle which will explain
why the atoms should tend, according to any
law, to the general centre, must be admitted as
satisfactorily explaining, at the same time, why,
according to the same law, they should tend each
to each. For, in fact, the tendency to the general centre is not to a centre as such, but because of its being a point in tending towards
which each atom tends most directly to its real
and essential centre, *Unity*—the absolute and
final Union of all.

The consideration here involved presents to
my own mind no embarrassment whatever—but
this fact does not blind me to the possibility of
its being obscure to those who may have been
less in the habit of dealing with abstractions:
—and, upon the whole, it may be as well to look
at the matter from one or two other points of
view.

The absolute, irrelative particle primarily
created by the Volition of God, must have been
in a condition of postive *normality*, or rightful-
ness—for wrongfulness implies *relation*. Right
is positive; wrong is negative—is merely the
negation of right; as cold is the negation of
heat—darkness of light. That a thing may be
wrong, it is necessary that there be some other
thing in *relation* to which it *is* wrong—some
condition which it fails to satisfy; some
law which it violates; some being whom
it aggrieves. If there be no such being,
law, or condition, in respect to which the

* Page 46.

thing is wrong—and, still more especially, if no beings, laws, or conditions exist at all—then the thing can*not* be wrong, and consequently must be *right*. Any deviation from normality involves a tendency to return to it. A difference from the normal—from the right—from the just —can be understood as affected only by the overcoming a difficulty; and if the force which overcomes the difficulty be not infinitely continued, the ineradicable tendency to return will at length be permitted to act for its own satisfaction. Upon withdrawal of the force, the tendency acts. This is the principle of reaction as the inevitable consequence of finite action. Employing a phraseology of which the seeming affectation will be pardoned for its expressiveness, we may say that Reaction is the return from the condition of *as it is and ought not to be* into the condition of *as it was, originally, and therefore ought to be:* —and let me add here that the *absolute* force of Reaction would no doubt be always found in direct proportion with the reality—the truth— the absoluteness—of the *originality*—if ever it were possible to measure this latter:—and, consequently, the greatest of all conceivable reactions must be that produced by the tendency which we now discuss—the tendency to return into the *absolutely original*—into the *supremely* primitive. Gravity, then, *must be the strongest of forces*—an idea reached *a priori* and abundantly confirmed by induction. What use I make of the idea, will be seen in the sequel.

The atoms, now, having been diffused from

their normal condition of Unity, seek to return
to——what? Not to any particular *point*, certainly; for it is clear that if, upon the diffusion,
the whole Universe of matter had been projected,
collectively, to a distance from the point of irradiation, the atomic tendency to the general centre
of the sphere would not have been disturbed in
the least:—the atoms would not have sought the
point *in absolute space* from which they were
originally impelled. It is merely the *condition,*
and not the point or locality at which this condition took its rise, that these atoms seek to re-
establish;—it is merely *that condition which is
their normality,* that they desire. "But they
seek a centre," it will be said, "and a centre is
a point." True; but they seek this point not
in its character of point—(for, were the whole
sphere moved from its position, they would seek,
equally, the centre; and the centre *then* would be
a *new point*)—but because it so happens, on
account of the form in which they collectively
exist—(that of the sphere)—that only *through*
the point in question—the sphere's centre—they
can attain their true object, Unity. In the direction of the centre each atom perceives more
atoms than in any other direction. Each atom
is impelled towards the centre because along the
straight line joining it and the centre and passing on to the circumference beyond, there lie a
greater number of atoms than along any other
straight line—a greater number of objects that
seek it, the individual atom—a greater number
of tendencies to Unity—a greater number of sat-

isfactions for its own tendency to Unity—in a word, because in the direction of the centre lies the utmost possibility of satisfaction, generally, for its own individual appetite. To be brief, the *condition*, Unity, is all that is really sought; and if the atoms *seem* to seek the centre of the sphere, it is only impliedly, through implication—because such centre happens to imply, to include, or to involve, the only essential centre, Unity. But *on account of* this implication or involution, there is no possibility of practically separating the tendency to Unity in the abstract, from the tendency to the concrete centre. Thus the tendency of the atoms to the general centre *is*, to all practical intents and for all logical purposes, the tendency each to each; and the tendency each to each *is* the tendency to the centre; and the one tendency may be assumed *as* the other; whatever will apply to the one must be thoroughly applicable to the other; and, in conclusion, whatever principle will satisfactorily explain the one, cannot be questioned as an explanation of the other.

In looking carefully around me for a rational objection to what I have advanced, I am able to discover *nothing:*—but of that class of objections usually urged by the doubters for Doubt's sake, I very readily perceive *three;* and proceed to dispose of them in order.

It may be said, first: "That the proof that the force of irradiation (in the case described) is directly proportional to the squares of the distances, depends upon an unwarranted assumption—that of the number of atoms in each stratum being the measure of the force with which they are emitted.''

I reply, not only tha⁺ I am warranted in such assumption, but that I should be utterly *unwar-*ranted in any other. What I assume is, simply, that an effect is the measure of its cause—that every exercise of the Divine Will will be proportional to that which demands the exertion—that the means of Omnipotence, or of Omniscience, will be exactly adapted to its purposes. Neither can a deficiency nor an excess of cause bring to pass any effect. Had the force which irradiated any stratum to its position, been either more or less than was needed for the purpose—that is to say, not *directly proportional* to the purpose—then to its position that stratum could not have been irradiated. Had the force which, with a view to general equability of distribution, emitted the proper number of atoms for each stratum, been not *directly proportional* to the number, then the number would *not* have been the number demanded for the equable distribution.

The second supposable objection is somewhat better entitled to an answer.

It is an admitted principle in Dynamics that every body, on receiving an impulse, or disposition to move, will move onward in a straight line, in the direction imparted by the impelling force, until deflected, or stopped, by some other force. How then, it may be asked, is my first or external stratum of atoms to be understood as discontinuing their movement at the circumference of the

IX. 5

imaginary glass sphere when no second force, of
more than an imaginary character, appears, to
account for the discontinuance?

I reply that the objection, in this case, actually
does arise out of "an unwarranted assumption"
—on the part of the objector—the assumption of
a principle, in Dynamics, at an epoch when *no*
"principles," in *anything,* exist:—I use the
word "principle," of course, in the objector's
understanding of the word.

"In the beginning" we can admit—indeed we
can comprehend—but one *First Cause*—the truly
ultimate *Principle*—the Volition of God. The
primary *act*—that of Irradiation from Unity—
must have been independent of all that which the
world now calls "principle"—because all that
we so designate is but a consequence of the reaction of that primary act:—I say *"primary"* act;
for the creation of the absolute material particle
is more properly to be regarded as a *conception*
than as an *"act"* in the ordinary meaning of the
term.   Thus, we must regard the primary act as
an act for the establishment of what we now call
"principles."   But this primary act itself is to
be considered as *continuous Volition.*   The
Thought of God is to be understood as originating the Diffusion—as proceeding with it—as reg-
ulating it—and, finally, as being withdrawn
from it upon its completion.   *Then* commences
Reaction, and through Reaction, "Principle," as
we employ the word.   It will be advisable, however, to limit the application of this word to the
two *immediate* results of the discontinuance of

the Divine Volition—that is, to the two agents, *Attraction* and *Repulsion*. Every other Natural agent depends, either more or less immediately, upon these two, and therefore would be more conveniently designated as *sub*-principle.

It may be objected, thirdly, that, in general, the peculiar mode of distribution which I have suggested for the atoms, is "an hypothesis and nothing more."

Now, I am aware that the word hypothesis is a ponderous sledge-hammer, grasped immediately, if not lifted, by all very diminutive thinkers, upon the first appearance of any proposition wearing, in any particular, the garb of *a theory*. But "hypothesis" cannot be wielded *here* to any good purpose, even by those who succeed in lifting it—little men or great.

I maintain, first, that *only* in the mode described is it conceivable that Matter could have been diffused so as to fulfil at once the conditions of irradiation and of generally equable distribution. I maintain, secondly, that these conditions themselves have been imposed upon me, as necessities, in a train of ratiocination *as rigorously logical as that which establishes any demonstration in Euclid;* and I maintain, thirdly, that even if the charge of "hypothesis" were as fully sustained as it is, in fact, unsustained and untenable, still the validity and indisputability of my result would not, even in the slightest particular, be disturbed.

To explain:—The Newtonian Gravity—a law of Nature—a law whose existence as such no one

out of Bedlam questions—a law whose admission
as such enables us to account for nine-tenths of
the Universal phænomena—a law which, merely
because it does so enable us to account for these
phænomena, we are perfectly willing, without
reference to any other considerations, to admit,
and cannot help admitting, as a law—a law, nevertheless, of which neither the principle nor the
modus operandi of the principle, has ever yet
been traced by the human analysis—a law, in
short, which, neither in its detail nor in its generality, has been found susceptible of explanation
at all—is at length seen to be at every point thoroughly explicable, provided we only yield our as-
sent to——what? To an hypothesis? Why *if* an
hypothesis—if the merest hypothesis—if an hypothesis for whose assumption—as in the case of
that *pure* hypothesis the Newtonian law itself—no
shadow of *a priori* reason could be assigned—if
an hypothesis, even as absolute as all this implies,
would enable us to perceive a principle for the
Newtonian law—would enable us to understand
as satisfied, conditions so miraculously—so inef-
fably complex and seemingly irreconcilable as
those involved in the relations of which Gravity
tells us,—what rational being *could* so expose his
fatuity as to call even this absolute hypothesis an
hypothesis any longer—unless, indeed, he were
to persist in so calling it, with the understanding
that he did so, simply for the sake of consistency
in words?

But what is the true state of our present case?
What is *the fact?* Not only that is *not* an hy-

pothesis which we are required *to adopt,* in order
to admit the principle at issue explained, but
that it *is* a logical conclusion which we are re-
quested *not* to adopt if we can avoid it—which
we are simply invited to *deny if we can:*—a conclusion of so accurate a logicality that to dispute
it would be the effort—to doubt its validity, beyond our power:—a conclusion from which we
see no mode of escape, turn as we will; a result
which confronts us either at the end of an *in-*
ductive journey from the phænomena of the very
Law discussed, or at the close of a *deductive* career from the most rigorously simple of all conceivable assumptions—*the assumption, in a
word, of Simplicity itself.*

And if here, for the mere sake of cavilling, it
be urged, that although my starting-point is, as
I assert, the assumption of absolute Simplicity,
yet Simplicity, considered merely in itself, is no
axiom; and that only deductions from axioms
are indisputable—it is thus that I reply:—

Every other science than Logic is the science
of certain concrete relations. Arithmetic, for
example, is the science of the relations of number
—Geometry, of the relations of form—Mathematics in general, of the relations of quantity in
general—of whatever can be increased or diminished. Logic, however, is the science of Relation
in the abstract—of absolute Relation—of Relation considered solely in itself. An axiom in any
particular science other than Logic is, thus, merely a proposition announcing certain concrete relations which seem to be too obvious for dispute

—as when we say, for instance, that the whole is
greater than its part;—and, thus again, the principle of the *Logical* axiom—in other words, of an
axiom in the abstract—is, simply, *obviousness of
relation.* Now, it is clear, not only that what is
obvious to one mind may not be obvious to another, but that what is obvious to one mind at
one epoch, may be anything but obvious, at another epoch, to the same mind. It is clear, moreover, that what, to-day, is obvious even to the majority of mankind, or to the majority of the best
intellects of mankind, may to-morrow be, to
either majority, more or less obvious, or in no respect obvious at all. It is seen, then, that the *axiomatic principle* itself is susceptible of variation, and of course that axioms are susceptible of
similar change. Being mutable, the "truths"
which grow out of them are necessarily mutable
too; or, in other words, are never to be positively
depended upon as truths at all—since Truth and
Immutability are one.

It will now be readily understood that no axiomatic idea—no idea founded in the fluctuating
principle, obviousness of relation—can possibly
be so secure—so reliable a basis for any structure
erected by the Reason, as *that* idea—(whatever it
is, wherever we can find it, or *if* it be practicable
to find it anywhere)—which is *ir*relative altogether—which not only presents to the understanding *no obviousness* of relation, either greater or less, to be considered, but subjects the intellect, not in the slightest degree, to the necessity
of even looking at *any relation at all.* If such an

idea be not what we too heedlessly term "an axiom," it is at least preferable, as a Logical basis, to any axiom ever propounded, or to all imaginable axioms combined:—and such, precisely, is the idea with which my deductive process, so thoroughly corroborated by induction, commences. My *particle proper* is but *absolute Irrelation.* To sum up what has been advanced:—As a starting point I have taken it for granted, simply, that the Beginning had nothing behind it or before it—that it was a Beginning in fact—that it was a beginning and nothing different from a beginning—in short, that this Beginning was—*that which it was.* If this be a "mere assumption" then a "mere assumption" let it be.

To conclude this branch of the subject:—I am fully warranted in announcing that *the Law which we have been in the habit of calling Gravity exists on account of Matter's having been irradiated, at its origin, atomically, into a limited* sphere of Space, from one, individual, unconditional, irrelative, and absolute Particle Proper, by the sole process in which it was possible to satisfy, at the same time, the two conditions, irradiation, and generally-equable distribution throughout the sphere—that is to say, by a force varying in direct proportion with the squares of the distances between the irradiated atoms, respectively, and the Particular centre of Irradiation.*

I have already given my reasons for presum-

---

* "Limited sphere"—A sphere is *necessarily* limited. I prefer tautology to a chance of misconception.

ing Matter to have been diffused by a determinate rather than by a continuous or infinitely continued force. Supposing a continuous force, we should be unable, in the first place, to comprehend a reaction at all; and we should be required, in the second place, to entertain the impossible conception of an infinite extension of Matter. Not to dwell upon the impossibility of the conception, the infinite extension of Matter is an idea which, if not positively disproved, is at least not in any respect warranted by telescopic observation of the stars—a point to be explained more fully hereafter; and this empirical reason for believing in the original finity of Matter is unempirically confirmed. For example:—Admitting, for the moment, the possibility of understanding Space *filled* with the irradiated atoms—that is to say, admitting, as well as we can, for argument's sake, that the succession of the irradiated atoms had absolutely *no end*—then it is abundantly clear that, even when the Volition of God had been withdrawn from them, and thus the tendency to return into Unity permitted (abstractly) to be satisfied, this permission would have been nugatory and invalid—practically valueless and of no effect whatever. No Reaction could have taken place; no movement toward Unity could have been made; no Law of Gravity could have obtained.

To explain:—Grant the *abstract* tendency of any one atom to any one other as the inevitable result of diffusion from the normal Unity:—or, what is the same thing, admit any given atom as *proposing* to move in any given direction—it is clear that, since there is an *infinity* of atoms on all sides of the atom proposing to move, it never can actually move toward the satisfaction of its tendency in the direction given, on account of a precisely equal and counter-balancing tendency in the direction diametrically opposite. In other words, exactly as many tendencies to Unity are behind the hesitating atom as before it; for it is a mere sotticism to say that one infinite line is longer or shorter than another infinite line, or that one infinite number is greater or less than another number that is infinite. Thus the atom in question must remain stationary forever. Under the impossible circumstances which we have been merely endeavoring to conceive for argument's sake, there could have been no aggregation of Matter—no stars—no worlds—nothing but a perpetually atomic and inconsequential Universe. In fact, view it as we will, the whole idea of unlimited Matter is not only untenable, but impossible and preposterous.

With the understanding of a *sphere* of atoms, however, we perceive, at once, a *satisfiable* tendency to union. The general result of the tendency each to each, being a tendency of all to the centre, the *general* process of condensation, or approximation, commences immediately, by a common and simultaneous movement, on withdrawal of the Divine Volition; the *individual* approximations, or coalescences—*not* coalitions —of atom with atom, being subject to almost infinite variations of time, degree, and condition,

on account of the excessive multiplicity of relation, arising from the differences of form assumed as characterizing the atoms at the moment
of their quitting the Particle Proper; as well as
from the subsequent particular inequidistance,
each from each.

What I wish to impress upon the reader is the
certainty of there arising, at once, (on withdrawal of the diffusive force, or Divine Volition,) out of the condition of the atoms as described, at innumerable points throughout the
Universal sphere, innumerable agglomerations,
characterized by innumerable specific differences
of form, size, essential nature, and distance each
from each. The development of Repulsion (Electricity) must have commenced, of course, with
the very earliest particular efforts at Unity, and
must have proceeded constantly in the ratio of
Coalescence—that is to say, *in that of Condensation,* or, again, of Heterogeneity.

Thus the two Principles Proper, *Attraction*
and *Repulsion*—the Material and the Spiritual
—accompany each other, in the strictest fellow-
ship, forever. Thus, *the Body and the Soul walk
hand in hand.*

If now, in fancy, we select *any one* of the agglomerations considered as in their primary
stages throughout the Universal sphere, and suppose this incipient agglomeration to be taking
place at that point where the centre of our Sun
exists—or rather where it *did* exist originally;
for the Sun is perpetually shifting his position—
we shall find ourselves met, and borne onward

for a time at least, by the most magnificent of theories—by the Nebular Cosmogony of Laplace:—although "Cosmogony" is far too comprehensive a term for what he really discusses—which is the constitution of our solar system alone—of one among the myriad of similar systems which make up the Universe Proper—that Universal sphere—that all-inclusive and absolute *Kosmos* which forms the subject of my present Discourse.

Confining himself to an *obviously limited* region—that of our solar system with its comparatively immediate vicinity—and *merely* assuming —that is to say, assuming without any basis whatever, either deductive or inductive—*much* of what I have been just endeavoring to place upon a more stable basis than assumption; assuming, for example, matter as diffused (without pretending to account for the diffusion) throughout, and somewhat beyond, the space occupied by our system—diffused in a state of heterogeneous nebulosity and obedient to that omniprevalent law of Gravity at whose principle he ventured to make no guess; assuming all this (which is quite true, although he had no logical right to its assumption) Laplace has shown, dynamically and mathematically, that the results in such case necessarily ensuing, are those and those alone which we find manifested in the actually existing condition of the system itself.

To explain:—Let us conceive *that* particular agglomeration of which we have just spoken—the one at the point designated by our Sun's centre

—to have so far proceeded that a vast quantity of nebulous matter has here assumed a roughly globular form; its centre being, of course, coincident with what is now, or rather was originally, the centre of our Sun; and its periphery extending out beyond the orbit of Neptune, the most remote of our planets:—in other words, let us suppose the diameter of this rough sphere to be some 6000 millions of miles. For ages, this mass of matter has been undergoing condensation, until at length it has become reduced into the bulk we imagine; having proceeded gradually, of course, from its atomic and imperceptible state, into what we understand of visible, palpable, or otherwise appreciable nebulosity.

Now, the condition of this mass implies a rotation about an imaginary axis—a rotation which, commencing with the absolute incipiency of the aggregation, has been ever since acquiring velocity. The very first two atoms which met, approaching each other from points not diametrically opposite, would, in rushing partially past each other, form a nucleus for the rotary movement described. How this would increase in velocity, is readily seen. The two atoms are joined by others:—an aggregation is formed. The mass continues to rotate while condensing. But any atom at the circumference has, of course, a more rapid motion than one nearer the centre. The outer atom, however, with its superior velocity, approaches the centre; carrying this superior velocity with it as it goes. Thus every atom, proceeding inwardly, and finally attaching itself to the condensed centre, adds something to the original velocity of that centre—that is to say, increases the rotary movement of the mass.

Let us now suppose this mass so far condensed that it occupies *precisely* the space circumscribed by the orbit of Neptune, and that the velocity with which the surface of the mass moves, in the general rotation, is precisely that velocity with which Neptune now revolves about the Sun. At this epoch, then, we are to understand that the constantly increasing centrifugal force, having gotten the better of the non-increasing centripetal, loosened and separated the exterior and least condensed stratum, or a few of the exterior and least condensed strata, at the equator of the sphere, where the tangential velocity predominated; so that these strata formed about the main body an independent ring encircling the equatorial regions:—just as the exterior portion thrown off, by excessive velocity of rotation, from a grindstone, would form a ring about the grindstone, but for the solidity of the superficial material: were this caoutchouc, or anything similar in consistency, precisely the phænomenon I describe would be presented.

The ring thus whirled from the nebulous mass, *revolved*, of course, *as* a separate ring, with just that velocity with which, while the surface of the mass, it *rotated*. In the meantime, condensation still proceeding, the interval between the discharged ring and the main body continued to increase, until the former was left at a vast distance from the latter.

Now, admitting the ring to have possessed, by some seemingly accidental arrangement of its heterogeneous materials, a constitution nearly uniform, then this ring, *as* such, would never have ceased revolving about its primary; but, as might have been anticipated, there appears to have been enough irregularity in the disposition of the materials, to make them cluster about centres of superior solidity; and thus the annular form was destroyed.* No doubt, the band was soon broken up into several portions, and one of these portions, predominating in mass, absorbed the others into itself; the whole settling, spherically, into a planet. That this latter, *as* a planet, continued the revolutionary movement which characterized it while a ring, is sufficiently clear; and that it took upon itself, also, an additional movement in its new condition of sphere, is readily explained. The ring being understood as yet unbroken, we see that its exterior, while the whole revolves about the parent body, moves more rapidly than its interior. When the rupture occurred, then, some portion in each fragment must have been moving with greater velocity than the others. The superior movement prevailing, must have whirled each fragment round—that is to say, have caused it to rotate; and the direction of the rotation must, of course, have been the direc-

---

* Laplace assumed his nebulosity heterogeneous, merely that he might be thus enabled to account for the breaking up of the rings; for had the nebulosity been homogeneous, they would not have broken. I reach the same result—heterogeneity of the secondary masses immediately resulting from the atoms—purely from an *a priori* consideration of their general design—*Relation.*

tion of the revolution whence it arose. *All* the
fragments having become subject to the rotation
described, must, in coalescing, have imparted it
to the one planet constituted by their coalescence.
—This planet was Neptune. Its material continuing to undergo condensation, and the centrifugal force generated in its rotation, getting,
at length, the better of the centripetal, as before
in the case of the parent orb, a ring was whirled
also from the equatorial surface of this planet:
this ring, having been uniform in its constitution, was broken up, and its several fragments,
being absorbed by the most massive, were collectively spherified into a moon. Subsequently,
the operation was repeated, and a second moon
was the result. We thus account for the planet
Neptune, with the two satellites which accompany him.

In throwing off a ring from its equator, the
Sun re-established that equilibrium between its
centripetal and centrifugal forces which had been
disturbed in the process of condensation; but, as
this condensation still proceeded, the equilibrium
was again immediately disturbed, through the increase of rotation. By the time the mass had
so far shrunk that it occupied a spherical space
just that circumscribed by the orbit of Uranus,
we are to understand that the centrifugal force
had so far obtained the ascendency that new relief was needed: a second equatorial band was,
consequently, thrown off, which, proving ununiform, was broken up, as before in the case of
Neptune; the fragments settling into the planet

Uranus; the velocity of whose actual revolution
about the Sun indicates, of course, the rotary
speed of that Sun's equatorial surface at the moment of the separation. Uranus, adopting a rotation from the collective rotations of the fragments composing it, as previously explained, now
threw off ring after ring; each of which, becoming broken up, settled into a moon:—three
moons, at different epochs, having been formed,
in this manner, by the rupture and general
spherification of as many distinct ununiform
rings.

By the time the Sun had shrunk until it occupied a space just that circumscribed by the orbit
of Saturn, the balance, we are to suppose, between its centripetal and contrifugal forces had
again become so far disturbed, through increase
of rotary velocity, the result of condensation,
that a third effort at equilibrium became necessary; and an annular band was therefore whirled
off, as twice before; which, on rupture through
ununiformity, became consolidated into the
planet Saturn. This latter threw off, in the first
place, seven uniform bands, which, on rupture,
were spherified respectively into as many moons;
but, subsequently, it appears to have discharged,
at three distinct but not very distant epochs,
three rings whose equability of constitution was,
by apparent accident, so considerable as to present no occasion for their rupture; thus they
continue to revolve as rings. I use the phrase
"*apparent* accident;" for of accident in the ordinary sense there was, of course, nothing:—the

term is properly applied only to the result of indistinguishable or not immediately traceable *law.*

Shrinking still farther, until it occupied just the space circumscribed by the orbit of Jupiter, the Sun now found need of farther effort to restore the counterbalance of its two forces, continually disarranged in the still continued increase of rotation. Jupiter, accordingly, was now thrown off; passing from the annular to the planetary condition; and, on attaining this latter, threw off in its turn, at four different epochs, four rings, which finally resolved themselves into so many moons.

Still shrinking, until its sphere occupied just the space defined by the orbit of the Asteroids, the Sun now discarded a ring which appears to have had *eight* centres of superior solidity, and, on breaking up, to have separated into eight fragments, no one of which so far predominated in mass as to absorb the others. All therefore, as distinct although comparatively small planets, proceeded to revolve in orbits whose distances, each from each, may be considered as in some degree the measure of the force which drove them asunder:—all the orbits, nevertheless, being so closely coincident as to admit of our calling them *one,* in view of the other planetary orbits.

Continuing to shrink, the Sun, on becoming so small as just to fill the orbit of Mars, now discharged this planet—of course by the process repeatedly described. Having no moon, however, Mars could have thrown off no ring. In fact,

IX. 6

an epoch had now arrived in the career of the
parent body, the centre of the system. The decrease of its nebulosity, which is the increase of
its density, and which again is the decrease of its
condensation, out of which latter arose the constant disturbance of equilibrium—must, by this
period, have attained a point at which the efforts
for restoration would have been more and more
ineffectual just in proportion as they were less
frequently needed. Thus the processes of which
we have been speaking would everywhere show
signs of exhaustion—in the planets, first, and secondly, in the original mass. We must not fall
into the error of supposing the decrease of interval observed among the planets as we approach
the Sun, to be in any respect indicative of an increase of frequency in the periods at which they
were discarded. Exactly the converse is to be
understood. The longest interval of time must
have occurred between the discharges of the two
interior; the shortest, between those of the two
exterior, planets. The decrease of the interval
of space is, nevertheless, the measure of the density, and thus inversely of the condensation, of
the Sun, throughout the processes detailed.

Having shrunk, however, so far as to fill only
the orbit of our Earth, the parent sphere whirled
from itself still one other body—the Earth—in a
condition so nebulous as to admit of this body's
discarding, in its turn, yet another, which is our
Moon;—but here terminated the lunar forma-
tions.

Finally, subsiding to the orbits first of Venus

and then of Mercury, the Sun discarded these two interior planets; neither of which has given birth to any moon.

Thus from his original bulk—or, to speak more accurately, from the condition in which we first considered him—from a partially spherified nebular mass, *certainly* much more than 5,600 millions of miles in diameter—the great central orb and origin of our solar-planetary-lunar system, has gradually descended, by condensation, in obedience to the law of Gravity, to a globe only 882,000 miles in diameter; but it by no means follows, either that its condensation is yet complete, or that it may not still possess the capacity of whirling from itself another planet.

I have here given—in outline of course, but still with all the detail necessary for distinctness—a view of the Nebular Theory as its author himself conceived it. From whatever point we regard it, we shall find it *beautifully true*. It is by far too beautiful, indeed, *not* to possess Truth as its essentiality—and here I am very profoundly serious in what I say. In the revolution of the satellites of Uranus, there does appear something seemingly inconsistent with the assumptions of Laplace; but that *one* inconsistency can invalidate a theory constructed from a million of intricate consistencies, is a fancy fit only for the fantastic. In prophesying, confidently, that the apparent anomaly to which I refer, will, sooner or later, be found one of the strongest possible corroborations of the general hypothesis, I pretend to no especial spirit of divination. It is a matter which the only difficulty seems *not* to foresee.*

The bodies whirled off in the processes described, would exchange, it has been seen, the superficial *rotation* of the orbs whence they originated, for a *revolution* of equal velocity about these orbs as distant centres; and the revolution thus engendered must proceed, so long as the centripetal force, or that with which the discarded body gravitates toward its parent, is neither greater nor less than that by which it was discarded; that is, than the centrifugal, or, far more properly, than the tangential, velocity. From the unity, however, of the origin of these two forces, we might have expected to find them as they are found—the one accurately counterbalancing the other. It has been shown, indeed, that the act of whirling-off is, in every case, merely an act for the preservation of the counterbalance.

After referring, however, the centripetal force to the omniprevalent law of Gravity, it has been the fashion with astronomical treatises, to seek beyond the limits of mere Nature—that is to say, of *Secondary* Cause—a solution of the phænomenon of tangential velocity. This latter they attribute directly to a *First* Cause—to God. The force which carries a steller body around its primary they assert to have originated in an impulse given immediately by the finger—this is the childish phraseology employed—by the finger

* I am prepared to show that the anomalous revolution of the satellites of Uranus is a simply perspective anomaly arising from the inclination of the axis of the planet.

of Deity itself. In this view, the planets, fully
formed, are conceived to have been hurled from
the Divine hand, to a position in the vicinity of
the suns, with an impetus mathematically adapted to the masses, or attractive capacities, of the
suns themselves. An idea so grossly unphilosophical, although so supinely adopted, could have
arisen only from the difficulty of otherwise accounting for the absolutely accurate adaptation,
each to each, cf two forces so seemingly independent, one of the other, as are the gravitating
and tangential. But it should be remembered
that, for a long time, the coincidence between the
moon's rotation and her sidereal revolution—two
matters seemingly far more independent than
those now considered—was looked upon as positively miraculous; and there was a strong disposition, even among astronomers, to attribute
the marvel to the direct and continual agency of
God—who, in this case, it was said, had found it
necessary to interpose, specially, among his general laws, a set of subsidiary regulations, for the
purpose of forever concealing from mortal eyes
the glories, or perhaps the horrors, of the other
side of the Moon—of that mysterious hemisphere
which has always avoided, and must perpetually
avoid, the telescopic scrutiny of mankind. The
advance of Science, however, soon demonstrated
—what to the philosophical instinct needed *no*
demonstration—that the one movement is but a
portion—something more, even, than a consequence—of the other.

For my part, I have no patience with fantasies

at once so timorous, so idle, and so awkward. They belong to the veriest *cowardice* of thought. That Nature and the God of Nature are distinct, no thinking being can long doubt. By the former we imply merely the laws of the latter. But with the very idea of God, omnipotent, omniscient, we entertain, also, the idea of *the infallibility* of his laws. With Him there being neither Past nor Future—with Him all being *Now*—do we not insult him in supposing his laws so contrived as not to provide for every possible contingency?—or, rather, what idea *can* we have of *any* possible contingency, except that it is at once a result and a manifestation of his laws? He who, divesting himself of prejudice, shall have the rare courage to think absolutely for himself, cannot fail to arrive, in the end, at the condensation of *laws* into *Law*—cannot fail of reaching the conclusion that *each law of Nature is dependent at all points upon all other laws,* and that all are but consequences of one primary exercise of the Divine Volition. Such is the principle of the Cosmogony which, with all necessary deference, I here venture to suggest and to maintain.

In this view, it will be seen that, dismissing as frivolous, and even impious, the fancy of the tangential force having been imparted to the planets immediately by "the finger of God," I consider this force as originating in the rotation of the stars:—this rotation as brought about by the in-rushing of the primary atoms, towards their respective centres of aggregation:—this in-rushing as the consequence of the law of Gravity:—this law as but the mode in which is necessarily manifested the tendency of the atoms to return into imparticularity:—this tendency to return as but the inevitable reaction of the first and most sublime of Acts—that act by which a God, self-existing and alone existing, became all things at once, through dint of his volition, while all things were thus constituted a portion of God.

The radical assumptions of this Discourse suggest to me, and in fact imply, certain important *modifications* of the Nebular Theory as given by Laplace. The efforts of the repulsive power I have considered as made for the purpose of preventing contact among the atoms, and thus as made in the ratio of the approach to contact—that is to say, in the ratio of condensation.* In other words, *Electricity,* with its involute phænomena, heat, light and magnetism, is to be understood as proceeding as condensation proceeds, and, of course, inversely, as destiny proceeds, or the *cessation to condense.* Thus the Sun, in the process of its aggregation, must soon, in developing repulsion, have become excessively heated—perhaps incandescent: and we can perceive how the operation of discarding its rings must have been materially assisted by the slight incrustation of its surface consequent on cooling. Any common experiment shows us how readily a crust of the character suggested, is separated, through heterogeneity. from the interior mass.

* Page 74

But, on every successive rejection of the crust, the new surface would appear incandescent as before; and the period at which it would again become so far incrusted as to be readily loosened and discharged, may well be imagined as exactly coincident with that as which a new effort would be needed, by the whole mass, to restore the equilibrium of its two forces, disarranged through condensation. In other words:—by the time the electric influence (Repulsion) has prepared the surface for rejection, we are to understand that the gravitating influence (Attraction) is precisely ready to reject it. Here, then, as everywhere, *the Body and the Soul walk hand in hand.*

These ideas are empirically confirmed at all points. Since condensation can never, in any body, be considered as absolutely at an end, we are warranted in anticipating that, whenever we have an opportunity of testing the matter, we shall find indications of resident luminosity in *all* the stellar bodies—moons and planets as well as suns. That our Moon is strongly self-luminous, we see at every total eclipse, when, if not so, she would disappear. On the dark part of the satellite, too, during her phases, we often observe flashes like our own Auroras; and that these latter, with our various other so-called electrical phænomena, without reference to any more steady radiance, must give our Earth a certain appearance of luminosity to an inhabitant of the Moon, is quite evident. In fact, we should regard all the phænomena referred to, as mere

manifestations, in different moods and degrees,
of the Earth's feebly-continued condensation.

If my views are tenable, we should be prepared
to find the newer planets—that is to say, those
nearer the Sun—more luminous than those older
and more remote:—and the extreme brilliancy
of Venus (on whose dark portions, during her
phases, the Auroras are frequently visible) does
not seem to be altogether accounted for by her
mere proximity to the central orb. She is no
doubt vividly self-luminous, although less so
than Mercury: while the luminosity of Neptune
may be comparatively nothing.

Admitting what I have urged, it is clear that,
from the moment of the Sun's discarding a ring,
there must be a continuous diminution both of
his heat and light, on account of the continuous
incrustation of his surface; and that a period
would arrive—the period immediately previous
to a new discharge—when a *very material* decrease of both light and heat, must become apparent. Now, we know that tokens of such
changes are distinctly recognisable. On the Mel-
ville islands—to adduce merely one out of a hundred examples—we find traces of *ultra-tropical*
vegetation—of plants that never could have
flourished without immensely more light and
heat than are at present afforded by our Sun to
any portion of the surface of the Earth. Is such
vegetation referable to an epoch immediately
subsequent to the whirling-off of Venus? At
this epoch must have occurred to us our greatest
access of solar influence; and. in fact, this in-

fluence must then have attained its maximum:—
leaving out of view, of course, the period when
the Earth itself was discarded—the period of its
mere organization.

Again:—we know that there exist *non-luminous suns*—that is to say, suns whose existence
we determine through the movements of others,
but whose luminosity is not sufficient to impress
us. Are these suns invisible merely on account
of the length of time elapsed since their discharge of a planet? And yet again:—may we
not—at least in certain cases—account for the
sudden appearances of suns where none had been
previously suspected, by the hypothesis that,
having rolled with incrusted surfaces throughout
the few thousand years of our astronomical history, each of these suns, in whirling off a new
secondary, has at length been enabled to display
the glories of its still incandescent interior?—
To the well-ascertained fact of the proportional
increase of heat as we descend into the Earth, I
need of course, do nothing more than refer:—it
comes in the strongest possible corroboration of
all that I have said on the topic now at issue.

In speaking, not long ago, of the repulsive or
electrical influence, I remarked that "the important phænomena of vitality, consciousness,
and thought, whether we observe them generally
or in detail, seem to proceed *at least in the ratio
of the heterogeneous.*"* I mentioned, too, that
I would recur to the suggestion:—and this is the
proper point at which to do so. Looking at the

* Page 38.

matter, first, in detail, we perceive that not merely the *manifestation* of vitality, but its importance, consequences, and elevation of character, keep pace, very closely, with the heterogeneity, or complexity, of the animal structure. Looking at the question, now, in its generality, and referring to the first movements of the atoms towards mass-constitution, we find that heterogeneousness, brought about directly through condensation, is proportional with it forever. We thus reach the proposition that *the importance of the development of the terrestrial vitality proceeds equably with the terrestrial condensation.*

Now this is in precise accordance with what we know of the succession of animals on the Earth. As it has proceeded in its condensation, superior and still superior races have appeared. Is it impossible that the successive geological revolutions which have attended, at least, if not immediately caused, these successive elevations of vitalic character—is it improbable that these revolutions have themselves been produced by the successive planetary discharges from the Sun —in other words, by the successive variations in the solar influence on the Earth? Were this idea tenable, we should not be unwarranted in the fancy that the discharge of yet a new planet, interior to Mercury, may give rise to yet a new modification of the terrestrial surface—a modification from which may spring a race both materially and spiritually superior to Man. These thoughts impress me with all the force of truth—

but I throw them out, of course, merely in their obvious character of suggestion.

The Nebular Theory of Laplace has lately received far more confirmation than it needed, at the hands of the philosopher, Comte. These two have thus together shown—*not,* to be sure, that Matter at any period actually existed as described, in a state of nebular diffusion, but that, admitting it so to have existed throughout the space and much beyond the space now occupied by our solar system, *and to have commenced a movement towards a centre*—it must gradually have assumed the various forms and motions which are now seen, in that system, to obtain. A demonstration such as this—a dynamical and mathematical demonstration, as far as demonstration can be—unquestionable and unquestioned—unless, indeed, by that unprofitable and disreputable tribe, the professional questioners— the mere madmen who deny the Newtonian law of Gravity on which the results of the French mathematicians are based—a demonstration, I say, such as this, would to most intellects be conclusive—and I confess that it is so to mine—of the validity of the nebular hypothesis upon which the demonstration depends.

That the demonstration does not *prove* the hypothesis, according to the common understanding of the word "proof," I admit, of course. To show that certain existing results—that certain established facts—may be, even mathematically, accounted for by the assumption of a certain hypothesis, is by no means to establish the hypothesis itself. In other words:—to show that, certain data being given, a certain existing result might, or even *must,* have ensued, will fail to prove that this result *did* ensue, *from the data,* until such time as it shall be also shown that there are, *and can be,* no other data from which the result in question might *equally* have ensued. But, in the case now discussed, although all must admit the deficiency of what we are in the habit of terming "proof," still there are many intellects, and those of the loftiest order, to which *no* proof could bring one iota of additional *conviction.* Without going into details which might impinge upon the Cloud-Land of Metaphysics, I may as well here observe, that the force of conviction, in cases such as this, will always, with the right-thinking, be proportional to the amount of *complexity* intervening between the hypothesis and the result. To be less abstract:— The greatness of the complexity found existing among cosmical conditions, by rendering great in the same proportion the difficulty of accounting for all these conditions, *at once,* strengthens, also in the same proportion, our faith in that hypothesis which does, in such manner, satisfactorily account for them:—and as *no* complexity can well be conceived greater than that of the astronomical conditions, so no conviction can be stronger—to *my* mind at least—than that with which I am impressed by an hypothesis that not only reconciles these conditions, with mathematical accuracy, and reduces them into a consistent and intelligible whole, but is, at the same time, the *sole* hypothesis by means of which the human intellect has been ever enabled to account for them *at all*.

A most unfounded opinion has been latterly current in gossiping and even in scientific circles —the opinion that the so-called Nebular Cosmogony has been overthrown. This fancy has arisen from the report of late observations made, among what hitherto have been termed the "nebulæ," through the large telescope of Cincinnati, and the world-renowned instrument of Lord Rosse. Certain spots in the firmament which presented, even to the most powerful of the old telescopes, the appearance of nebulosity, or haze, had been regarded for a long time as confirming the theory of Laplace. They were looked upon as stars in that very process of condensation which I have been attempting to describe. Thus it was supposed that we "had ocular evidence"—an evidence, by the way, which has always been found very questionable—of the truth of the hypothesis; and, although certain telescopic improvements, every now and then, enabled us to perceive that a spot, here and there, which we had been classing among the nebulæ, was, in fact, but a cluster of stars deriving its nebular character only from its immensity of distance—still it was thought that no doubt could exist as to the actual nebulosity of numerous other masses, the strong-holds of the nebulists, bidding defiance to every effort at segregation. Of these latter the most interesting was the great "nebula" in the constellation Orion:—but this,

with innumerable other miscalled "nebulæ,"
when viewed through the magnificent modern
telescopes, has become resolved into a simple collection of stars. Now this fact has been very
generally understood as conclusive against the
Nebular Hypothesis of Laplace; and, on announcement of the discoveries in question, the
most enthusiastic defender and most eloquent
popularizer of the theory, Dr. Nichol, went so
far as to "admit the necessity of abandoning"
an idea which had formed the material of his
most praiseworthy book.*

Many of my readers will no doubt be inclined
to say that the result of these new investigations
has at least a strong *tendency* to overthrow the
hypothesis; while some of them, more thought-
ful, will suggest that, although the theory is by
no means disproved through the segregation of
the particular "nebulæ" alluded to, still a *failure* to segregate them, with such telescopes,
might well have been understood as a triumphant
corroboration of the theory: and this latter class
will be surprised, perhaps, to hear me say that
even with *them* I disagree. If the propositions
of this Discourse have been comprehended, it will
be seen that, in my view, a failure to segregate

* "*Views of the Architecture of the Heavens.*" A letter,
purporting to be from Dr. Nichol to a friend in America, went
the rounds of our newspapers, about two years ago, I think,
admitting "the necessity" to which I refer. In a subsequent
Lecture, however, Dr. N. appears in some manner to have
gotten the better of the necessity, and does not quite *renounce*
the theory, although he seems to wish that he could sneer at
it as "a purely hypothetical one." What else was the Law
of Gravity before the Maskelyne experiments? and who questioned the Law of Gravity, even then?

the "nebulæ" would have tended to the refutation, rather than to the confirmation, of the Nebular Hypothesis.

Let me explain:—The Newtonian Law of Gravity we may, of course, assume as demonstrated. This law, it will be remembered, I have referred to the reaction of the first Divine Act —to the reaction of an exercise of the Divine Volition temporarily overcoming a difficulty. This difficulty is that of forcing the normal into the abnormal—of impelling that whose originality, and therefore whose rightful condition was *One,* to take upon itself the wrongful condition of *Many.* It is only by conceiving this difficulty as *temporarily* overcome, that we can comprehend a reaction. There could have been no reaction had the act been infinitely continued. So long as the act *lasted,* no reaction, of course, could commence; in other words, no *gravitation* could take place—for we have considered the one as but the manifestation of the other. But gravitation *has* taken place; therefore the act of Creation has ceased; and gravitation has long ago taken place; therefore the act of Creation has long ago ceased. We can no more expect, then, to observe *the primary processes* of Creation; and to these primary processes the condition of nebulosity has already been explained to belong.

Through what we know of the propagation of light, we have direct proof that the more remote of the stars have existed, under the forms in which we now see them, for an inconceivable

number of years. So far back *at least,* then, as
the period when these stars underwent condensation, must have been the epoch at which the
mass-constitutive processes began. That we may
conceive these processes, then, as still going on
in the case of certain "nebulæ," while in all
other cases we find them thoroughly at an end,
we are forced into assumptions for which we
have really *no* basis whatever—we have to thrust
in, again, upon the revolting Reason, the blas-
phemous idea, of special interposition—we have
to suppose that, in the particular instances of
these "nebulæ," an unerring God found it necessary to introduce certain supplementary regulations—certain improvements of the general
law—certain re-touchings and emendations, in
a word, which had the effect of deferring the
completion of these individual stars for centuries
of centuries beyond the æra during which all the
other stellar bodies had time, not only to be fully
constituted, but to grow hoary with an unspeak-
able old age.

Of course, it will be immediately objected that,
since the light by which we recognise the nebulæ
now must be merely that which left their surfaces a vast number of years ago, the processes
at present observed, or supposed to be observed,
are, in fact, *not* processes now actually going
on, but the phantoms of processes completed long
in the Past—just as I maintain all these mass-
constitutive processes *must* have been.

To this I reply that neither is the now-observed
condition of the condensed stars their actual con-

IX. 7

dition, but a condition completed long in the Past; so that my argument drawn from the *relative* condition of the stars and the ''nebulæ,'' is in no manner disturbed. Moreover, those who maintain the existence of nebulæ, do *not* refer the nebulosity to extreme distance; they declare it a real and not merely a perspective nebulosity. That we may conceive, indeed, a nebular mass as visible at all, we must conceive it as *very near us* in comparison with the condensed stars brought into view by the modern telescopes. In maintaining the appearances in question, then, to be really nebulous, we maintain their comparative vicinity to our point of view. Thus, their condition, as we see them now, must be referred to an epoch *far less remote* than that to which we may refer the now-observed condition of at least the majority of the stars.—In a word, should Astronomy ever demonstrate a ''nebula,'' in the sense at present intended, I should consider the Nebular Cosmogony—*not*, indeed, as corroborated by the demonstration—but as thereby irretrievably overthrown.

By way, however, of rendering unto Cæsar *no more* than the things that are Cæsar's, let me here remark that the assumption of the hypothesis which led him to so glorious a result, seems to have been suggested to Laplace in great measure by a misconception—by the very misconception of which we have just been speaking —by the generally prevalent misunderstanding of the character of the nebulæ, so mis-named. These he supposed to be, in reality, what their designation implies. The fact is, this great man had, very properly, an inferior faith in his own merely *perceptive* powers. In respect, therefore, to the actual existence of nebulæ—an existence so confidently maintained by his telescopic contemporaries—he depended less upon what he saw than upon what he heard.

It will be seen that the only valid objections to his theory, are those made to its hypothesis *as* such—to what suggested it—not to what it suggests; to its propositions rather than to its results. His most unwarranted assumption was that of giving the atoms a movement towards a centre, in the very face of his evident understanding that these atoms, in unlimited succession, extended throughout the Universal space. I have already shown that, under such circumstances, there could have occurred no movement at all; and Laplace, consequently, assumed one on no more philosophical ground that that something of the kind was necessary for the establishment of what he intended to establish.

His original idea seems to have been a compound of the true Epicurean atoms with the false nebulæ of his contemporaries; and thus his theory presents us with the singular anomaly of absolute truth deduced, as a mathematical result, from a hybrid datum of ancient imagination intertangled with modern inacumen. Laplace's real strength lay, in fact, in an almost miraculous mathematical instinct:—on this he relied; and in no instance did it fail or deceive him: —in the case of the Nebular Cosmogony, it led

him, blindfolded, through a labyrinth of Error,
into one of the most luminous and stupendous
temples of Truth.

Let us now fancy, for the moment, that the
ring first thrown off by the Sun—that is to say,
the ring whose breaking-up constituted Neptune
—did not, in fact, break up until the throwing-
off of the ring out of which Uranus arose; that
this latter ring, again, remained perfect until the
discharge of that out of which sprang Saturn;
that this latter, again, remained entire until the
discharge of that from which originated Jupiter—
and so on. Let us imagine, in a word, that no dissolution occurred among the rings until the final
rejection of that which gave birth to Mercury.
We thus paint to the eye of the mind a series
of coexistent concentric circles; and looking as
well at *them* as at the processes by which, according to Laplace's hypothesis, they were constructed, we perceive at once a very singular
analogy with the atomic strata and the process
of the original irradiation as I have described
it.   It is impossible that, on measuring the
forces, respectively, by which each successive
planetary circle was thrown off—that is to say,
on measuring the successive excesses of rotation
over gravitation which occasioned the successive
discharges—we should find the analogy in question more decidedly confirmed? *Is it improbable that we should discover these forces to have
varied—as in the original radiation—proportion-
ally to the squares of the distances?*

Our solar system, consisting, in chief, of one

sun, with sixteen planets certainly, and possibly
a few more, revolving about it at various distances, and attended by seventeen moons assuredly, but *very* probably by several others—is now
to be considered as *an example* of the innumerable agglomerations which proceeded to take
place throughout the Universal Sphere of atoms
on withdrawal of the Divine Volition. I mean
to say that our solar system is to be understood
as affording a *generic instance* of these agglomerations, or, more correctly, of the ulterior conditions at which they arrived. If we keep our
attention fixed on the idea of *the utmost possible
Relation* as the Omnipotent design, and on the
precautions taken to accomplish it through difference of form, among the original atoms, and
particular inequidistance, we shall find it impossible to suppose for a moment that even any two
of the incipient agglomerations reached precisely
the same result in the end. We shall rather be
inclined to think that *no two* stellar bodies in
the Universe—whether suns, planets or moons
—are particularly, while *all* are generally, similar. Still less, then, can we imagine any two
assemblages of such bodies—any two "systems"
—as having more than a general resemblance.*
Our telescopes, at this point, thoroughly confirm
our deductions. Taking our own solar system,

* It is not *impossible* that some unlooked-for optical improvement may disclose to us, among innumerable varieties
of systems, a luminous sun, encircled by luminous and non-
luminous rings, within and without and between which, revolve luminous and non-luminous planets, attended by moons
having moons—and even these latter again having moons.

then, as merely a loose or general type of all, we have so far proceeded in our subject as to survey the Universe under the aspect of a spherical space, throughout which, dispersed with merely general equability, exist a number of but generally similar *systems*.

Let us now, expanding our conceptions, look upon each of these systems as in itself an atom; which in fact it is, when we consider it as but one of the countless myriads of systems which constitute the Universe. Regarding all, then, as but colossal atoms, each with the same ineradicable tendency to Unity which characterizes the actual atoms of which it consists—we enter at once upon a new order of aggregations. The smaller systems, in the vicinity of a larger one, would, inevitably, be drawn into still closer vicinity. A thousand would assemble here; a million there—perhaps here, again, even a billion—leaving, thus, immeasurable vacancies in space. And if, now, it be demanded why, in the case of these systems—of these merely Titanic atoms—I speak, simply, of an "assemblage," and not, as in the case of the actual atoms, of a more or less consolidated agglomeration:—if it be asked, for instance, why I do not carry what I suggest to its legitimate conclusion, and describe, at once, these assemblages of system-atoms as rushing to consolidation in spheres—as each becoming condensed into one magnificent sun—my reply is that μέλλοντα ταῦτα*—I am but pausing, for a

---

*A quotation from the "Antigone" of Sophocles, meaning. "These things are of the future."—EDITOR.

moment, on the awful threshold of *the Future*.
For the present, calling these assemblages "clusters," we see them in the incipient stages of their consolidation. Their *absolute* consolidation is *to come*.

We have now reached a point from which we behold the Universe as a spherical space, interspersed, *unequably*, with *clusters*. It will be noticed that I here prefer the adverb "unequably" to the phrase "with a merely general equability," employed before. It is evident, in fact, that the equability of distribution will diminish in the ratio of the agglomerative processes—that is to say, as the things distributed diminish in number. Thus the increase of *inequability*—an increase which must continue until, sooner or later, an epoch will arrive at which the largest agglomeration will absorb all the others—should be viewed as, simply, a corroborative indication of the *tendency to One*.

And here, at length, it seems proper to inquire whether the ascertained *facts* of Astronomy confirm the general arrangement which I have thus, deductively, assigned to the Heavens. Thoroughly, they *do*. Telescopic observation, guided by the laws of perspective, enables us to understand that the perceptible Universe exists as *a cluster of clusters, irregularly disposed*.

The "clusters" of which this Universal "*cluster of clusters*" consists, are merely what we have been in the practice of designating "nebulæ"—and, of these "nebulæ," *one* is of paramount interest to mankind. I allude to the

Galaxy, or Milky Way. This interests us, first and most obviously, on account of its great superiority in apparent size, not only to any one other cluster in the firmament, but to all the other clusters taken together. The largest of these latter occupies a mere point, comparatively, and is distinctly seen only with the aid of a telescope. The Galaxy sweeps throughout the Heaven and is brilliantly visible to the naked eye. But it interests man chiefly, although less immediately, on account of its being his home; the home of the Earth on which he exists; the home of the Sun about which this Earth revolves; the home of that "system" of orbs of which the Sun is the centre and primary—the Earth one of sixteen secondaries, or planets—the Moon one of seventeen tertiaries, or satellites. The Galaxy, let me repeat, is but one of the *clusters* which I have been describing—but one of the mis-called "nebulæ" revealed to us—by the telescope alone, sometimes—as faint hazy spots in various quarters of the sky. We have no reason to suppose the Milky Way *really* more extensive than the least of these "nebulæ." Its vast superiority in size is but an apparent superiority arising from our position in regard to it—that is to say, from our position in its midst. However strange the assertion may at first appear to those unversed in Astronomy, still the astronomer himself has no hesitation in asserting that we are *in the midst* of that inconceivable host of stars—of suns—of systems— which constitute the Galaxy. Moreover, not only have *we*—not only has *our*

Sun a right to claim the Galaxy as its own especial cluster, but, with slight reservation, it may
be said that all the distinctly visible stars of the
firmament—all the stars visible to the naked eye
—have equally a right to claim it as *their* own.

There has been a great deal of misconception
in respect to the *shape* of the Galaxy; which, in
nearly all our astronomical treatises, is said to re-
semble that of a capital Y. The cluster in question has, in reality, a certain general—*very* general resemblance to the planet Saturn, with its
encompassing triple ring. Instead of the solid
orb of that planet however, we must picture to
ourselves a lenticular star-island, or collection of
stars; our Sun lying excentrically—near the
shore of the island—on that side of it which is
nearest the constellation of the Cross and farthest from that of Cassiopeia. The surrounding
ring, where it approaches our position, has in it
a longitudinal *gash,* which does, in fact, cause *the
ring, in our vicinity,* to assume, loosely, the appearance of a capital Y.

We must not fall into the error, however, of
conceiving the somewhat indefinite girdle as at
all *remote,* comparatively speaking, from the also
indefinite lenticular cluster which it surrounds;
and thus, for mere purpose of explanation, we
may speak of our Sun as actually situated at that
point of the Y where its three component lines
unite; and, conceiving this letter to be of a certain solidity—of a certain thickness, very trivial
in comparison with its length—we may even
speak of our position as *in the middle* of this

thickness. Fancying ourselves thus placed, we shall no longer find difficulty in accounting for the phænomena presented—which are perspective altogether. When we look upward or downward—that is to say, when we cast our eyes in the direction of the letter's *thickness*—we look through fewer stars than when we cast them in the direction of its *length,* or *along* either of the three component lines. Of course, in the former case, the stars appear scattered—in the latter, crowded.—To reverse this explanation:—An inhabitant of the Earth, when looking, as we commonly express ourselves, *at* the Galaxy, is then beholding it in some of the directions of its length—is looking *along* the lines of the Y—but when, looking out into the general Heaven, he turns his eyes *from* the Galaxy, he is then surveying it in the direction of the letter's thickness; and on this account the stars seem to him scattered; while, in fact, they are as close together, on an average, as in the mass of the cluster. *No* consideration could be better adapted to convey an idea of this cluster's stupendous extent.

If, with a telescope of high space-penetrating power, we carefully inspect the firmament, we shall become aware of *a belt of clusters*—of what we have hitherto called "nebulæ"—a *band,* of varying breadth, stretching from horizon to horizon, at right angles to the general course of the Milky Way. This band is the ultimate *cluster of clusters.* This belt is *The Universe.* Our Galaxy is but one, and perhaps one of the most inconsiderable, of the clusters which go to the constitution of this ultimate, Universal *belt* or *band*. The appearance of this cluster of clusters, to our eyes, *as* a belt or band, is altogether a perspective phænomenon of the same character as that which causes us to behold our own individual and roughly-spherical cluster, the Galaxy, under guise also of a belt, traversing the Heavens at right angles to the Universal one. The shape of the all-inclusive cluster is, of course *generally,* that of each individual cluster which it includes. Just as the scattered stars which, on looking *from* the Galaxy, we see in the general sky, are, in fact, but a portion of that Galaxy itself, and as closely intermingled with it as any of the telescopic points in what seems the densest portion of its mass—so are the scattered "nebulæ" which, on casting our eyes *from* the Universal *belt,* we perceive at all points of the firmament—so, I say, are these scattered "nebulæ" to be understood as only perspectively scattered, and as part and parcel of the one supreme and Universal *sphere.*

No astronomical fallacy is more untenable, and none has been more pertinaciously adhered to, than that of the absolute *illimitation* of the Universe of Stars. The reasons for limitation, as I have already assigned them, *a priori,* seem to me unanswerable; but, not to speak of these, *observation* assures us that there is, in numerous directions around us, certainly, if not in all, a positive limit—or, at the very least, affords us no basis whatever for thinking otherwise. Were the succession of stars endless, then the background

of the sky would present us a uniform luminosity, like that displayed by the Galaxy—*since
there could be absolutely no point, in all that
background, at which would not exist a star.*
The only mode, therefore, in which, under such a
state of affairs, we could comprehend the *voids*
which our telescopes find in innumerable directions, would be by supposing the distance of the
invisible background so immense that no ray
from it has yet been able to reach us at all. That
this *may* be so, who shall venture to deny? I
maintain, simply, that we have not even the
shadow of a reason for believing that it *is* so.

When speaking of the vulgar propensity to
regard all bodies on the Earth as tending merely
to the Earth's centre, I observed that, "with certain exceptions to be specified hereafter, every
body on the Earth tended not only to the Earth's
centre, but in every conceivable direction besides."* The "exceptions" refer to those frequent gaps in the Heavens, where our utmost
scrutiny can detect not only no stellar bodies,
but no indications of their existence:—where
yawning chasms, blacker than Erebus, seem to
afford us glimpses, through the boundary walls
of the Universe of Stars, into the illimitable
Universe of Vacancy, beyond. Now as any body,
existing on the Earth, chances to pass, either
through its own movement or the Earth's, into a
line with any one of these voids, or cosmical
abysses, it clearly is no longer attracted *in the direction of that void*, and for the moment, conse-

* Page 42.

quently, is "heavier" than at any period, either
after or before. Independently of the consideration of these voids, however, and looking only at
the generally unequable distribution of the stars,
we see that the absolute tendency of bodies on the
Earth to the Earth's centre, is in a state of perpetual variation.

We comprehend, then, the insulation of our
Universe. We perceive the isolation of *that*—
of *all* that which we grasp with the senses. We
know that there exists one *cluster of clusters*—a
collection around which, on all sides, extend the
immeasurable wildernesses of a Space *to all
human perception* untenanted. But *because*
upon the confines of this Universe of Stars we
are compelled to pause, through want of farther
evidence from the senses, is it right to conclude
that, in fact, there *is* no material point beyond
that which we have thus been permitted to attain? Have we, or have we not, an analogical
right to the inference that this perceptible Universe—that this cluster of clusters—is but one of
a series of clusters of clusters, the rest
of which are invisible through distance—
through the diffusion of their light being
so excessive, ere it reaches us, as not to
produce upon our retinas a light impression—
or from there being no such emanation as light at
all, in these unspeakably distant worlds—or, last-
ly, from the mere interval being so vast, that the
electric tidings of their presence in Space, have
not yet—through the lapsing myriads of years—
been enabled to traverse that interval?

Have we any right to inferences—have we any ground whatever for visions such as these? If we have a right to them in *any* degree, we have a right to their infinite extension.

The human brain has obviously a leaning to the *"Infinite,"* and fondles the phantom of the idea. It seems to long with a passionate fervor for this impossible conception, with the hope of intellectually believing it when conceived. What is general among the whole race of Man, of course no individual of that race can be warranted in considering abnormal; nevertheless, there *may* be a class of superior intelligences, to whom the human bias alluded to may wear all the character of monomania.

My question, however, remains unanswered:—Have we any right to infer—let us say, rather, to imagine—an interminable succession of the "cluster of clusters," or of "Universes" more or less similar?

I reply that the "right," in a case such as this, depends absolutely upon the hardihood of that imagination which ventures to claim the right. Let me declare, only, that, as an individual, I myself feel impelled to *fancy*—without daring to call it more—that there *does* exist a *limitless* succession of Universes, more or less similar to that of which we have cognizance—to that of which *alone* we shall ever have cognizance—at the very least until the return of our own particular Universe into Unity. *If* such clusters of clusters exist, however—*and they do*—it is abundantly clear that, having had no part in our origin, they have no portion in our laws. They neither attract us, nor we them. Their material—their spirit is not ours—is not that which obtains in any part of our Universe. They could not impress our senses or our souls. Among them and us—considering all, for the moment, collectively—there are no influences in common. Each exists, apart and independently, *in the bosom of its proper and particular God.*

In the conduct of this Discourse, I am aiming less at physical than at metaphysical order. The clearness with which even material phænomena are presented to the understanding, depends very little, I have long since learned to perceive, upon a merely natural, and almost altogether upon a moral, arrangement. If then I seem to step somewhat too discursively from point to point of my topic, let me suggest that I do so in the hope of thus the better keeping unbroken that chain of *graduated impression* by which alone the intellect of Man can expect to encompass the grandeurs of which I speak, and, in their majestic totality, to comprehend them.

So far, our attention has been directed, almost exclusively, to a general and relative grouping of the stellar bodies in space. Of specification there has been little; and whatever ideas of *quantity* have been conveyed—that is to say, of number, magnitude, and distance—have been conveyed incidentally and by way of preparation for more definite conceptions. These latter let us now attempt to entertain.

Our solar system, as has been already men-

tioned, consists, in chief, of one sun and sixteen
planets certainly, but in all probability a few
others, revolving around it as a centre, and attended by seventeen moons of which we know,
with possibly several more of which as yet we
know nothing. These various bodies are not true
spheres, but oblate spheroids—spheres flattened
at the poles of the imaginary axes about which
they rotate:—the flattening being a consequence
of the rotation. Neither is the Sun absolutely the
centre of the system; for this Sun itself, with all
the planets, revolves about a perpetually shifting
point of space, which is the system's general centre of gravity. Neither are we to consider the
paths through which these different spheroids
move—the moons about the planets, the planets
about the Sun, or the Sun about the common centre—as circles in an accurate sense. They are, in
fact, *ellipses—one of the foci being the point
about which the revolution is made*. An ellipse
is a curve, returning into itself, one of whose di-
ameters is longer than the other. In the longer
diameter are two points, equidistant from the
middle of the line, and so situated otherwise that
if, from each of them a straight line be drawn to
any one point of the curve, the two lines, taken
together, will be equal to the long diameter itself.
Now let us conceive such an ellipse. At one of
the points mentioned, which are the *foci*, let us
fasten an orange. By an elastic thread let us
connect this orange with a pea; and let us place
this latter on the circumference of the ellipse.
Let us now move the pea continuously around

the orange—keeping always on the circumference of the ellipse. The elastic thread, which, of course, varies in length as we move the pea, will form what in geometry is called a *radius vector*. Now, if the orange be understood as the Sun, and the pea as a planet revolving about it, then the revolution should be made at such a rate—with a velocity so varying—that the *radius vector* may pass over *equal areas of space in equal times*. The progress of the pea *should be*—in other words, the progress of the planet *is*, of course,—slow in proportion to its distance from the Sun—swift in proportion to its proximity. Those planets, moreover, move the more slowly which are the farther from the Sun; *the squares of their periods of revolution having the same proportion to each other, as have to each other the cubes of their mean distances from the Sun.*

The wonderfully complex laws of revolution here described, however, are not to be understood as obtaining in our system alone. They *everywhere* prevail where Attraction prevails. They control *the Universe.* Every shining speck in the firmament is, no doubt, a luminous Sun, resembling our own, at least in its general features, and having in attendance upon it a greater or less number of planets, greater or less, whose still lingering luminosity is not sufficient to render them visible to us at so vast a distance, but which, nevertheless, revolve, moon-attended, about the starry centres, in obedience to the principles just detailed—in obedience to the three omniprevalent laws of revolution—the three im-

IX. 8

mortal laws *guessed* by the imaginative Kepler, and but subsequently demonstrated and accounted for by the patient and mathematical Newton. Among a tribe of philosophers who pride themselves excessively upon matter-of-fact, it is far too fashionable to sneer at all speculation under the comprehensive *sobriquet*, "guesswork." The point to be considered is, *who* guesses. In guessing with Plato, we spend our time to better purpose, now and then, than in harkening to a demonstration by Alcmæon.

In many works on Astronomy I find it distinctly stated that the laws of Kepler are *the basis* of the great principle, Gravitation. This idea must have arisen from the fact that the suggestion of these laws by Kepler, and his proving them *a posteriori* to have an actual existence, led Newton to account for them by the hypothesis of Gravitation, and, finally, to demonstrate them *a priori*, as necessary consequences of the hypothetical principle. Thus so far from the laws of Kepler being the basis of Gravity, Gravity is the basis of these laws—as it is, indeed, of all the laws, of the material Universe which are not referable to Repulsion alone.

The mean distance of the Earth from the Moon—that is to say, from the heavenly body in our closest vicinity—is 237,000 miles. Mercury, the planet nearest the Sun, is distant from him 37 millions of miles. Venus, the next, revolves at a distance of 68 millions:—the Earth, which comes next, at a distance of 95 millions: —Mars, then, at a distance of 144 millions. Now

come the eight Asteroids (Ceres, Juno, Vesta,
Pallas, Astræa, Flora, Iris, and Hebe) at an
average distance of about 250 millions. Then we
have Jupiter, distant 490 millions; then Saturn,
900 millions; then Uranus, 19 hundred millions;
finally Neptune, lately discovered, and revolving
at a distance, say of 28 hundred millions. Leaving Neptune out of the account—of which as yet
we know little accurately and which is, possibly,
one of a system of Asteroids—it will be seen that,
within certain limits, there exists an *order of
interval* among the planets. Speaking loosely,
we may say that each outer planet is twice as
far from the Sun as is the next inner one. May
not the *order* here mentioned—*may not the law
of Bode—be deduced from consideration of the
analogy suggested by me as having place between
the solar discharge of rings and the mode of the
atomic irradiation?*

The numbers hurriedly mentioned in this sum-
mary of distance, it is folly to attempt comprehending, unless in the light of abstract arithmet-
ical facts. They are not practically tangible
ones. They convey no precise ideas. I have
stated that Neptune, the planet farthest from
the Sun, revolves about him at a distance of 28
hundred millions of miles. So far good:—I
have stated a mathematical fact; and, without
comprehending it in the least, we may put it to
use—mathematically. But in mentioning, even,
that the Moon revolves about the Earth at the
comparatively trifling distance of 237,000 miles,
I entertained no expectation of giving any one

to understand—to know—to feel—how far from
the Earth the Moon actually *is*. 237,000 *miles!*
There are, perhaps, few of my readers who have
not crossed the Atlantic ocean; yet how many of
them have a distinct idea of even the 3,000 miles
intervening between shore and shore? I doubt,
indeed, whether the man lives who can force into
his brain the most remote conception of the interval between one milestone and its next neigh-
bor upon the turnpike. We are in some measure
aided, however, in our consideration of distance,
by combining this consideration with the kin-
dred one of velocity. Sound passes through
1100 feet of space in a second of time. Now
were it possible for an inhabitant of the Earth
to see the flash of a cannon discharged in the
Moon, and to hear the report, he would have to
wait, after perceiving the former, more than 13
entire days and nights before getting any intimation of the latter.

However feeble be the impression, even thus
conveyed, of the Moon's real distance from the
Earth, it will, nevertheless, effect a good object
in enabling us more clearly to see the futility
of attempting to grasp such intervals as that
of the 28 hundred millions of miles between our
Sun and Neptune; or even that of the 95 millions between the Sun and the Earth we inhabit.
A cannon-ball, flying at the greatest velocity with
which such a ball has ever been known to fly,
could not traverse the latter interval in less than
20 years; while for the former it would require
590.

Our Moon's real diameter is 2160 miles; yet
she is comparatively so trifling an object that it
would take nearly 50 such orbs to compose one
as great as the Earth.

The diameter of our own globe is 7912 miles
—but from the enunciation of these numbers
what positive idea do we derive?

If we ascend an ordinary mountain and look
around us from its summit, we behold a land-
scape stretching, say 40 miles, in every direction;
forming a circle 250 miles in circumference; and
including an area of 5000 square miles. The extent of such a prospect, on account of the *suc-
cessiveness* with which its portions necessarily
present themselves to view, can be only very
feebly and very partially appreciated:—yet the
entire panorama would comprehend no more than
one 40,000th part of the mere *surface* of our
globe.   Were this panorama, then, to be succeeded, after the lapse of an hour, by another
of equal extent; this again by a third, after
the lapse of an hour; this again by a fourth
after lapse of another hour—and so on, until
the scenery of the whole Earth were exhausted;
and were we to be engaged in examining these
various panoramas for twelve hours of every
day; we should nevertheless, be 9 nine years and
48 days in completing the general survey.

But if the mere surface of the Earth eludes
the grasp of the imagination, what are we to
think of its cubical contents?   It embraces a
mass of matter equal in weight to at least two
sextillions, two hundred quintillions of tons. Let

us suppose it in a state of quiescence; and now let us endeavor to conceive a mechanical force sufficient to set it in motion! Not the strength of all the myriads of beings whom we may conclude to inhabit the planetary worlds of our systems—not the combined physical strength of *all* these beings—even admitting all to be more powerful than man—would avail to stir the ponderous mass *a single inch* from its position.

What are we to understand, then, of the force, which under similar circumstances, would be required to move the *largest* of our planets, Jupiter? This is 86,000 miles in diameter, and would include within its periphery more than a thousand orbs of the magnitude of our own. Yet this stupendous body is actually flying around the Sun at the rate of 29,000 miles an hour—that is to say, with a velocity forty times greater than that of a cannot-ball! The thought of such a phænomenon cannot well be said to *startle* the mind:—it palsies and appals it. Not unfrequently we task our imagination in picturing the capacities of an angel. Let us fancy such a being at a distance of some hundred miles from Jupiter—a close eye-witness of this planet as it speeds on its annual revolution. Now *can* we, I demand, fashion for ourselves any conception so distinct of this ideal being's spiritual exaltation, as *that* involved in the supposition that, even by this immeasurable mass of matter, whirled immediately before his eyes, with a velocity so unutterable, he—an angel—angelic though he be—

is not at once struck into nothingness and overwhelmed?

At this point, however, it seems proper to suggest that, in fact, we have been speaking of comparative trifles. Our Sun—the central and controlling orb of the system to which Jupiter belongs—is not only greater than Jupiter, but greater by far than all the planets of the system taken together. This fact is an essential condition, indeed, of the stability of the system itself. The diameter of Jupiter has been mentioned: it is 86,000 miles:—that of the Sun is 882,000 miles. An inhabitant of the latter, travelling ninety miles a day, would be more than eighty years in going round a great circle of its circumference. It occupies a cubical space of 681 quadrillions, 472 trillions of miles. The Moon, as has been stated, revolves about the Earth at a distance of 237,000 miles—in an orbit, consequently, of nearly a million and a half. Now, were the Sun placed upon the Earth, centre over centre, the body of the former would extend, in every direction, not only to the line of the Moon's orbit, but beyond it, a distance of 200,000 miles.

And here, once again, let me suggest that, in fact, we have *still* been speaking of comparative trifles. The distance of the planet Neptune from the Sun has been stated: it is 28 hundred millions of miles: the circumference of its orbit, therefore, is about 17 billions. Let this be borne in mind while we glance at some one of the brightest stars. Between this and the star of *our* system, (the Sun,) there is a gulf of space, to convey any idea of which, we should need the tongue of an archangel. From *our* system, then, and from *our* Sun, or star, the star at which we suppose ourselves glancing is a thing altogether apart:—still, for the moment, let us imagine it placed upon our Sun, centre over centre, as we just now imagined this Sun itself placed upon the Earth. Let us now conceive the particular star we have in mind, extending, in every direction, beyond the orbit of Mercury— of Venus—of the Earth:—still *on,* beyond the orbit of Mars—of Jupiter—of Uranus—until, finally, we fancy it filling the circle—*seventeen billions of miles in circumference*—which is described by the revolution of Leverrier's planet. When we have conceived all this, we shall have entertained no extravagant conception. There is the very best reason for believing that many of the stars are even far larger than the one we have imagined. I mean to say, that we have the very best *empirical* basis for such belief:—and, in looking back at the original, atomic arrangements for *diversity*, which have been assumed as a part of the Divine plan in the constitution of the Universe, we shall be enabled easily to understand, and to credit, the existence of even far vaster disproportions in stellar size than any to which I have hitherto alluded. The largest orbs, of course, we must expect to find rolling through the widest vacancies of Space.

I remarked, just now, that to convey an idea of the interval between our Sun and any one of the other stars, we should require the eloquence of an archangel. In so saying, I should not be accused of exaggeration; for, in simple truth, these are topics on which it is scarcely possible to exaggerate. But let us bring the matter more distinctly before the eye of the mind.

In the first place, we may get a general, *relative* conception of the interval referred to, by comparing it with the inter-planetary spaces. If, for example, we suppose the Earth, which is, in reality, 95 millions of miles from the Sun, to be only *one foot* from that luminary; then Neptune would be forty feet distant; *and the star Alpha Lyræ, at the very least, one hundred and fifty-nine.*

Now I presume that, in the termination of my last sentence, few of my readers have noticed anything especially objectionable—particularly wrong. I said that the distance of the Earth from the Sun being taken at *one foot,* the distance of Neptune would be forty feet, and that of Alpha Lyræ, one hundred and fifty-nine. The proportion between one foot and one hundred and fifty-nine, has appeared, perhaps, to convey a sufficiently definite impression of the proportion between the two intervals—that of the Earth from the Sun, and that of Alpha Lyræ from the same luminary. But my account of the matter should, in reality, have run thus:— The distance of the Earth from the Sun being taken at one foot, the distance of Neptune would be forty feet, and that of Alpha Lyræ, one hundred and fifty-nine——*miles:*—that is to say, I had assigned to Alpha Lyræ, in my first state-

ment of the case, only the 5280th part of that distance which is the *least distance possible* at which
it can actually lie.

To proceed:—However distant a mere *planet*
is, yet when we look at it through a telescope, we
see it under a certain form—of a certain appreciable size. Now I have already hinted at the
probable bulk of many of the stars; nevertheless,
when we view any one of them, even through
the most powerful telescope, it is found to present us with *no form,* and consequently with *no
magnitude* whatever. We see it as a point, and
nothing more.

Again:—Let us suppose ourselves walking, at
night, on a highway. In a field on one side of the
road, is a line of tall objects, say trees, the figures
of which are distinctly defined against the background of the sky. This line of objects extends
at right angles to the road, and from the road to
the horizon. Now, as we proceed along the road,
we see these objects changing their positions, respectively, in relation to a certain fixed point in
that portion of the firmament which forms the
background of the view. Let us suppose this fixed
point—sufficiently fixed for our purpose—to be
the rising moon. We become aware, at once,
that while the tree nearest us so far alters its
position in respect to the moon, as to seem flying
behind us, the tree in the extreme distance has
scarcely changed at all its relative position with
the satellite. We then go on to perceive that the
farther the objects are from us, the less they
alter their positions; and the converse. Then

we begin, unwittingly, to estimate the distances
of individual trees by the degrees in which they
evince the relative alteration. Finally, we come
to understand how it might be possible to ascertain the actual distance of any given tree in the
line, by using the amount of relative alteration
as a basis in a simple geometrical problem. Now,
this relative alteration is what we call "parallax;" and by parallax we calculate the distances
of the heavenly bodies. Applying the principle
to the trees in question, we should, of course, be
very much at a loss to comprehend the distance
of *that* tree, which, however far we proceeded
along the road, should evince *no* parallax at all.
This, in the case described, is a thing impossible;
but impossible only because all distances on our
Earth are trivial indeed:—in comparison with
the vast cosmical quantities, we may speak of
them as absolutely nothing.

Now, let us suppose the star Alpha Lyræ
directly overhead; and let us imagine that, instead of standing on the Earth, we stand at one
end of a straight road stretching through Space
to a distance equalling the diameter of the
Earth's orbit—that is to say, to a distance of
one hundred and ninety millions of miles. Having observed, by means of the most delicate mi-
crometrical instruments, the exact position of the
star, let us now pass along this inconceivable
road, until we reach the other extremity. Now,
once again, let us look at the star. It is *precisely*
where we left it. Our instruments, however delicate, assure us that its relative position is abso-

lutely—is identically the same, as at the commencement of our unutterable journey. *No* parallax—none whatever—has been found.

The fact is, that, in regard to the distance of
the fixed stars—of any one of the myriads of
suns glistening on the farther side of that awful
chasm which separates our system from its broth-
ers in the cluster to which it belongs—astronomical science, until very lately, could speak only
with a negative certainty. Assuming the brightest as the nearest, we could say, even of *them,*
only that there is a certain incomprehensible distance on the *hither* side of which they cannot be:
—how far they are beyond it we had in no case
been able to ascertain. We perceived, for example, that Alpha Lyræ cannot be nearer to us than
19 trillions, 200 billions of miles; but, for all we
knew, and indeed for all we now know, it may
be distant from us the square, or the cube, or any
other power of the number mentioned. By dint,
however, of wonderfully minute and cautious observations, continued, with novel instruments,
for many laborious years, *Bessel,* not long ago
deceased, has lately succeeded in determining the
distance of six or seven stars; among others, that
of the star numbered 61 in the constellation of
the Swan. The distance in this latter instance
ascertained, is 670,000 times that of the Sun;
which last it will be remembered, is 95 millions
of miles. The star 61 Cygni, then, is nearly 64
trillions of miles from us—or more than three
times the distance assigned, *as the least possible,*
for Alpha Lyræ.

In attempting to appreciate this interval by
the aid of any considerations of *velocity,* as we
did in endeavoring to estimate the distance of the
moon, we must leave out of sight, altogether, such
nothings as the speed of a cannon ball, or of
sound. Light, however, according to the latest
calculations of Struve, proceeds at the rate of
167,000 miles in a second. Thought itself cannot
pass through this interval more speedily—if, indeed, thought can traverse it at all. Yet, in
coming from 61 Cygni to us, even at this inconceivable rate, light occupies more than *ten years;*
and, consequently, were the star this moment
blotted out from the Universe, still, *for ten years,*
would it continue to sparkle on, undimmed in its
paradoxical glory.

Keeping now in mind whatever feeble conception we may have attained of the interval between our Sun and 61 Cygni, let us remember
that this interval, however unutterably vast, we
are permitted to consider as but the *average* interval among the countless host of stars composing that cluster, or "nebula," to which our system, as well as that of 61 Cygni, belongs. I
have, in fact, stated the case with great modera-
tion:—we have excellent reason for believing 61
Cygni to be one of the *nearest* stars, and thus
for concluding, at least for the present, that its
distance from us is *less* than the average distance
between star and star in the magnificent cluster
of the Milky Way.

And here, once again and finally, it seems
proper to suggest that even as yet we have been

speaking of trifles. Ceasing to wonder at the space between star and star in our own or in any particular cluster, let us rather turn our thoughts to the intervals between cluster and cluster, in the all-comprehensive cluster of the Universe.

I have already said that light proceeds at the rate of 167,000 miles in a second—that is, about 10 millions of miles in a minute, or about 600 millions of miles in an hour:—yet so far removed from us are some of the "nebulæ" that even light, speeding with this velocity, could not and does not reach us, from those mysterious regions, in less than 3 *millions of years*. This calculation, moreover, is made by the elder Herschel, and in reference merely to those comparatively proximate clusters within the scope of his own telescope. There *are* "nebulæ," however, which, through the magical tube of Lord Rosse, are this instant whispering in our ears the secrets of *a million of ages* by-gone. In a word, the events which we behold now—at this moment—in those worlds—are the identical events which interested their inhabitants *ten hundred thousand centuries ago*. In intervals—in distances such as this suggestion force upon the *soul*—rather than upon the mind—we find, at length, a fitting climax to all hitherto frivolous considerations of *quantity*.

Our fancies thus occupied with the cosmical distances, let us take the opportunity of referring to the difficulty which we have so often experienced, while pursuing *the beaten path* of astronomical reflection, *in accounting* for the im-

measurable voids alluded to—in comprehending
why chasms so totally unoccupied and therefore
apparently so needless, have been made to inter-
vene between star and star—between cluster and
cluster—in understanding, to be brief, a sufficient reason for the Titanic scale, in respect of
mere *Space*, on which the Universe is seen to be
constructed. A rational cause for the phænomenon, I maintain that Astronomy has palpably
failed to assign:—but the considerations through
which, in this Essay, we have proceeded step by
step, enable us clearly and immediately to perceive that *Space and Duration are one.* That
the Universe might *endure* throughout an æra
at all commensurate with the grandeur of its
component material portions and with the high
majesty of its spiritual purposes, it was necessary that the original atomic diffusion be made
to so inconceivable an extent as to be only not
infinite. It was required, in a word, that the
stars should be gathered into visibility from invisible nebulosity—proceed from nebulosity to
consolidation—and so grow grey in giving birth
and death to unspeakably numerous and complex
variations of vitalic development:—it was required that the stars should do all this—should
have time thoroughly to accomplish all these
Divine purposes—*during the period* in which all
things were effecting their return into Unity
with a velocity accumulating in the inverse proportion of the squares of the distances at which
lay the inevitable End.

Throughout all this we have no difficulty in

understanding the absolute accuracy of the Divine *adaptation.* The density of the stars, respectively, proceeds, of course, as their condensation diminishes; condensation and heterogeneity keep pace with each other, through the latter, which is the index of the former, we estimate the vitalic and spiritual development. Thus, in the density of the globes, we have the measure in which their purposes are fulfilled. *As* density proceeds—*as* the Divine intentions *are* accomplished—*as* less and still less remains *to be* accomplished—so—in the same ratio—should we expect to find an acceleration of *the End:*—and thus the philosophical mind will easily comprehend that the Divine designs in constituting the stars, advance *mathematically* to their fulfilment:—and more; it will readily give the advance a mathematical expression; it will decide that this advance is inversely proportional with the squares of the distances of all created things from the starting-point and goal of their creation.

Not only is this Divine adaptation, however, mathematically accurate, but there is that about it which stamps it *as divine,* in distinction from that which is merely the work of human constructiveness. I allude to the complete *mutuality* of adaptation. For example; in human constructions a particular cause has a particular effect; a particular intention brings to pass a particular object; but this is all; we see no reciprocity. The effect does not re-act upon the cause; the intention does not change relations with the object. In Divine constructions the object is either design or object as we choose to regard it—and we may take at any time a cause for an effect, or the converse—so that we can never absolutely decide which is which.

To give an instance:—In polar climates the human frame, to maintain its animal heat, requires, for combustion in the capillary system, an abundant supply of highly azotized food, such as train-oil. But again:—in polar climates nearly the sole food afforded man is the oil of abundant seals and whales. Now, whether is oil at hand because imperatively demanded, or the only thing demanded because the only thing to be obtained? It is impossible to decide. There is an absolute *reciprocity of adaptation.*

The pleasure which we derive from any display of human ingenuity is in the ratio of *the approach* to this species of reciprocity. In the construction of *plot,* for example, in fictitious literature, we should aim at so arranging the incidents that we shall not be able to determine, of any one of them, whether it depends from any one other or upholds it. In this sense, of course, *perfection of plot* is really, or practically, unattainable—but only because it is a finite intelligence that constructs. The plots of God are perfect. The Universe is a plot of God.

And now we have reached a point at which the intellect is forced, again, to struggle against its propensity for analogical inference—against its monomaniac grasping at the infinite. Moons have been seen *revolving* about planets; planets

IX. 9

about stars; and the poetical instinct of human-ity—its instinct of the symmetrical, if the sym-metry be but a symmetry of surface:—this *in-stinct*, which the Soul, not only of Man but of all created beings, took up, in the beginning, from the *geometrical* basis of the Universal irradiation —impels us to the fancy of an endless extension of this system of *cycles*. Closing our eyes equally to *de*duction and *in*duction, we insist upon imag-ining a *revolution* of all the orbs of the Galaxy about some gigantic globe which we take to be the central pivot of the whole. Each cluster in the great cluster of clusters is imagined, of course, to be similarly supplied and constructed; while, that the "analogy" may be wanting at no point, we go on to conceive these clusters them-selves, again, as *revolving* about some still more august sphere;—this latter, still again, *with* its encircling clusters, as but one of a yet more mag-nificent series of agglomerations, *gyrating* about yet another orb central *to them*—some orb still more unspeakably sublime—some orb, let us rather say, of infinite sublimity endlessly multi-plied by the infinitely sublime. Such are the conditions, continued in perpetuity, which the voice of what some people term "analogy" calls upon the Fancy to depict and the Reason to con-template, if possible, without becoming dissatis-fied with the picture. Such, *in general*, are the interminable gyrations beyond gyration which we have been instructed by Philosophy to com-prehend and to account for, at least in the best manner we can. Now and then, however, a philosopher proper—one whose frenzy takes a very determinate turn—whose genius, to speak more reverentially, has a strongly-pronounced washer-womanish bias, doing every thing up by the dozen—enables us to see *precisely* that point out of sight, at which the revolutionary processes in question do, and of right ought to, come to an end.

It is hardly worth while, perhaps, even to sneer at the reveries of Fourrier:—but much has been said, latterly, of the hypothesis of Mädler—that there exists, in the centre of the Galaxy, a stupendous globe about which all the systems of the cluster revolve. The *period* of our own, indeed, has been stated—117 millions of years.

That our Sun has a motion in space, independently of its rotation, and revolution about the system's centre of gravity, has long been suspected. This motion, granting it to exist, would be manifested perspectively. The stars in that firmamental region which we were leaving behind us, would, in a very long series of years, become crowded; those in the opposite quarter, scattered. Now, by means of astronomical History, we ascertain, cloudily, that some such phænomena have occurred. On this ground it has been declared that our system is moving to a point in the heavens diametrically opposite the star Zeta Herculis:—but this inference is, perhaps, the maximum to which we have any logical right. Mädler, however, has gone so far as to designate a particular star, Alcyone in the

Pleiades, as being at or about the very spot around which a general *revolution* is performed.

Now, since by "analogy" we are led, in the first instance, to these dreams, it is no more than proper that we should abide by analogy, at least in some measure, during their development; and that analogy which suggests the revolution, suggests at the same time a central orb about which it should be performed:—so far the astronomer was consistent. This central orb, however, should, dynamically, be greater than all the orbs, taken together, which surround it. Of these there are about 100 millions. "Why, then," it was of course demanded, "do we not *see* this vast central sun—*at least equal* in mass to 100 millions of such suns as ours—why do we not *see* it—*we*, especially, who occupy the mid region of the cluster—the very locality *near* which, at all events, must be situated this incomparable star?" The reply was ready—"It must be non-luminous, as are our planets." Here, then, to suit a purpose, analogy is suddenly let fall. "Not so," it may be said—"we know that non-luminous suns actually exist." It is true that we have reason at least for supposing so; but we have certainly no reason whatever for supposing that the non-luminous suns in question are encircled by *luminous* suns, while these again are surrounded by non-luminous planets:—and it is precisely all this with which Mädler is called upon to find any thing analogous in the heavens —for it is precisely all this which he imagines in the case of the Galaxy. Admitting the thing to be so, we cannot help here picturing to ourselves how sad a puzzle the *why is it so* must prove to all *a priori* philosophers.

But granting, in the very teeth of analogy and of every thing else, the non-luminosity of the vast central orb, we may still inquire how this orb, so enormous, could fail of being rendered visible by the flood of light thrown upon it from the 100 millions of glorious suns glaring in all directions about it. Upon the urging of this question, the idea of an actually solid central sun appears, in some measure, to have been abandoned; and speculation proceeded to assert that the systems of the cluster perform their revolutions merely about an immaterial centre of gravity common to all. Here again then, to suit a purpose, analogy is let fall. The planets of our system revolve, it is true, about a common centre of gravity; but they do this in connection with, and in consequence of, a material sun whose mass more than counterbalances the rest of the system.

The mathematical circle is a curve composed of an infinity of straight lines. But this idea of the circle—an idea which, in view of all ordinary geometry, is merely the mathematical, as contra-distinguished from the practical, idea—is, in sober fact, the *practical* conception which alone we have any right to entertain in regard to the majestic circle with which we have to deal, at least in fancy, when we suppose our system revolving about a point in the centre of the Galaxy. Let the most vigorous of human imaginations attempt but to take a single step towards the comprehension of a sweep so ineffable! It would scarcely be paradoxical to say that a flash of lightning itself, travelling *forever* upon the circumference of this unutterable circle, would still, *forever*, be travelling in a straight line. That the path of our Sun in such an orbit would, to any human perception, deviate in the slightest degree from a straight line, even in a million of years, is a proposition not to be entertained: —yet we are required to believe that a curvature has become apparent during the brief period of our astronomical history—during a mere point —during the utter nothingness of two or three thousand years.

It may be said that Mädler *has* really ascertained a curvature in the direction of our system's now well-established progress through Space. Admitting, if necessary, this fact to be in reality such, I maintain that nothing is thereby shown except the reality of this fact—the fact of a curvature. For its *thorough* determination, ages will be required; and, when determined, it will be found indicative of some binary or other multiple relation between our Sun and some one or more of the proximate stars. I hazard nothing however, in predicting, that, after the lapse of many centuries, all efforts at determining the path of our Sun through Space, will be abandoned as fruitless. This is easily conceivable when we look at the infinity of perturbation it must experience, from its perpetually-shifting relations with other orbs, in the common approach of all to the nucleus of the Galaxy.

But in examining other "nebulæ" than that of the Milky Way—in surveying, generally, the clusters which overspread the heavens—do we or do we not find confirmation of Mädler's hypothesis? We do *not*. The forms of the clusters are exceedingly diverse when casually viewed; but on close inspection, through powerful telescopes, we recognise the sphere, very distinctly, as at least the proximate form of all:—their constitution, in general, being at variance with the idea of revolution about a common centre.

"It is difficult," says Sir John Herschel, "to form any conception of the dynamical state of such systems. On one hand, without a rotary motion and a centrifugal force, it is hardly possible not to regard them as in a state of *progressive collapse*. On the other, granting such a motion and such a force, we find it no less difficult to reconcile their forms with the rotation of the whole system [meaning cluster] around any single axis, without which internal collision would appear to be inevitable."

Some remarks lately made about the "nebulæ" by Dr. Nichol, in taking quite a different view of the cosmical conditions from any taken in this Discourse—have a very peculiar applicability to the point now at issue. He says:

"When our greatest telescopes are brought to bear upon them, we find that those which were thought to be irregular, are not so; they approach nearer to a globe. Here is one that looked oval; but Lord Rosse's telescope brought it into a circle. . . . Now there occurs a

very remarkable circumstance in reference to
these comparatively sweeping circular masses of
nebulæ. We find they are not entirely circular,
but the reverse; and that all around them, on
every side, there are volumes of stars, *stretching
out apparently as if they were rushing towards
a great central mass in consequence of the action
of some great power.*"*

Were I to describe, in my own words, what
must necessarily be the existing condition of each
nebula on the hypothesis that all matter is, as
I suggest, now returning to its original Unity, I
should simply be going over, nearly verbatim,
the language here employed by Dr. Nichol, without the faintest suspicion of that stupendous
truth which is the key to these nebular phænomena.

And here let me fortify my position still farther, by the voice of a greater than Mädler—
of one, moreover, to whom all the data of Mädler
have long been familiar things, carefully and
thoroughly considered. Referring to the elaborate calculations of Argelander—the very re-
searches which form Mädler's basis—*Humboldt*,
whose generalizing powers have never, perhaps,
been equalled, has the following observation:

"When we regard the real, proper, or non-
perspective motions of the stars, we find *many
groups of them moving in opposite directions;*

---

* I must be understood as denying, *especially*, only the
revolutionary portion of Mädler's hypothesis. Of course, if no
great central orb exists *now* in our cluster, such will exist
hereafter. Whenever existing, it will be merely the *nucleus*
of the consolidation.

and the data as yet in hand render it not necessary, at least, to conceive that the systems composing the Milky Way, or the clusters, generally, composing the Universe, are revolving about any particular centre unknown, whether luminous or non-luminous. It is but Man's longing for a fundamental First Cause, that impels both his intellect and fancy to the adoption of such an hypothesis."[*]

The phænomenon here alluded to—that of "many groups moving in opposite directions" —is quite inexplicable by Mädler's idea; but arises, as a necessary consequence, from that which forms the basis of this Discourse. While the *merely general direction* of each atom—of each moon, planet, star, or cluster—would, on my hypothesis, be, of course, absolutely rectilinear, while the *general* path of all bodies would be a right line leading to the centre of all; it is clear, nevertheless, that this general rectilinearity would be compounded of what, with scarcely any exaggeration, we may term an infinity of particular curves—an infinity of local deviations from rectilinearity—the result of continuous differences of relative position among the

* Betrachtet man die nicht perspectivischen eigenen Bewegungen der Sterne, so scheinen viele gruppenweise in ihrer Richtung entgegengesetzt; und die bisher gesammelten Thatsachen machen es auf's wenigste nicht nothwendig, anzunehmen, dass alle Theile unserer Sternenschicht oder gar der gesammten Sterneninseln, welche den Weltraum füllen, sich um einen grossen, unbekannten, leuchtenden oder dunkeln Centralkörper bewegen. Das Streben nach den letzten und höchsten Grundursachen macht freilich die reflectirende Thätigkeit des Menschen, wie seine Phantasie, zu einer solchen Annahme geneigt.

multitudinous masses, as each proceeded on its
own proper journey to the End.

I quoted, just now, from Sir John Herschel,
the following words, used in reference to the
clusters:—"On one hand, without a rotary
motion and a centrifugal force, it is hardly possible not to regard them as in a state of *progressive collapse.*" The fact is, that, in surveying
the "nebulæ" with a telescope of high power,
we shall find it quite impossible, having once conceived this idea of "collapse," not to gather, at
all points, corroboration of the idea. A nucleus
is always apparent, in the direction of which
the stars seem to be precipitating themselves;
nor can these nuclei be mistaken for merely perspective phænomena:—the clusters are *really*
denser near the centre—sparser in the regions
more remote from it. In a word, we see every
thing as we *should* see it were a collapse taking
place; but, in general, it may be said of these
clusters, that we can fairly entertain, while looking at them, the idea of *orbitual movement about
a centre,* only by admitting the *possible* existence, in the distant domains of space, of dynamical laws with which *we* are unacquainted.

On the part of Herschel, however, there is evi-
dently *a reluctance* to regard the nebulæ as in
"a state of progressive collapse." But if facts
—if even appearances justify the supposition of
their being in this state, *why,* it may well be
demanded, is he disinclined to admit it? Simply
on account of a prejudice;—merely because the
supposition is at war with a pre-conceived and

utterly baseless notion—that of the endlessness —that of the eternal stability of the Universe.

If the propositions of this Discourse are tenable, the "state of progressive collapse" is *precisely* that state in which alone we are warranted in considering All Things; and, with due humility, let me here confess that, for my part, I am at a loss to conceive how any *other* understanding of the existing condition of affairs could ever have made its way into the human brain. "The tendency to collapse," and "the attraction of gravitation" are convertible phrases. In using either, we speak of the reaction of the First Act. Never was necessity less obvious than that of supposing Matter imbued with an ineradicable *equality* forming part of its material nature—a quality, or instinct, *forever* inseparable from it, and by dint of which inalienable principle every atom is *perpetually* impelled to seek its fellow-atom. Never was necessity less obvious than that of entertaining this unphilosophical idea. Going boldly behind the vulgar thought, we have to conceive, metaphysically, that the gravitating principle appertains to Matter *temporarily*— only while diffused—only while existing as Many instead of as One—appertains to it by virtue of its state of irradiation alone—appertains, in a word, altogether to its *condition*, and not in the slightest degree to *itself*. In this view, when the irradiation shall have returned into its source —when the reaction shall be completed—the gravitating principle will no longer exist. And, in fact, astronomers, without at any time reaching the idea here suggested, seem to have been approximating it, in the assertion that "if there were but one body in the universe, it would be impossible to understand how the principle, Gravity, could obtain:" that is to say, from a consideration of Matter as they find it, they reach a conclusion at which I deductively arrive. That so pregnant a suggestion as the one quoted should have been permitted to remain so long unfruitful, is, nevertheless, a mystery which I find it difficult to fathom.

It is perhaps, in no little degree, however, our propensity for the continuous—for the analogical—in the present case more particularly for the symmetrical—which has been leading us astray. And, in fact, the sense of the symmetrical is an instinct which may be depended upon with an almost blindfold reliance. It is the poetical essence of the Universe—*of the Universe*, which, in the supremeness of its symmetry, is but the most sublime of poems. Now symmetry and consistency are convertible terms:— thus Poetry and Truth are one. A thing is consistent in the ratio of its truth—true in the ratio of its consistency. *A perfect consistency, I repeat, can be nothing but an absolute truth.* We may take it for granted, then, that Man cannot long or widely err, if he suffer himself to be guided by his poetical, which I have maintained to be his truthful, in being his symmetrical, instinct. He must have a care, however, lest, in pursuing too heedlessly the superficial symmetry of forms and motions, he leave out of sight the

really essential symmetry of the principles which
determine and control them.

That the stellar bodies would finally be merged
in one—that, at last, all would be drawn into
the substance of *one stupendous central orb already existing*—is an idea which, for some time
past, seems, vaguely and indeterminately, to have
held possession of the fancy of mankind. It is
an idea, in fact, which belongs to the class of the
excessively obvious. It springs, instantly, from
a superficial observation of the cyclic and seemingly *gyrating* or *vortical* movements of those
individual portions of the Universe which come
most immediately and most closely under our observation. There is not, perhaps, a human being,
of ordinary education and of average reflective
capacity, to whom, at some period, the fancy in
question has not occurred, as if spontaneously,
or intuitively, and wearing all the character of
a very profound and very original conception.
This conception, however, so commonly entertained, has never, within my knowledge, arisen
out of any abstract considerations. Being, on the
contrary, always suggested, as I say, by the vorticial movements about centres, a reason for it,
also,—a *cause* for the ingathering of all the orbs
into one, *imagined to be already existing*, was
naturally sought in the same direction—among
these cyclic movements themselves.

Thus it happened that, on announcement of
the gradual and perfectly regular decrease observed in the orbit of Encke's comet, at every
successive revolution about our Sun, astronomers

were nearly unanimous in the opinion that the cause in question was found—that a principle was discovered sufficient to account, physically, for that final, universal agglomeration which, I repeat, the analogical, symmetrical, or poetical instinct of man had pre-determined to understand as something more than a simple hypothesis.

This cause—this sufficient reason for the final ingathering—was declared to exist in an exceedingly rare but still material medium pervading space; which medium, by retarding, in some degree, the progress of the comet, perpetually weakened its tangential force; thus giving a predominance to the centripetal; which, of course, drew the comet nearer and nearer at each revolution, and would eventually precipitate it upon the Sun.

All this was strictly logical—admitting the medium or ether; but this ether was assumed, most illogically, on the ground that no *other* mode than the one spoken of could be discovered, of accounting for the observed decrease in the orbit of the comet:—as if from the fact that we could *discover* no other mode of accounting for it, it followed, in any respect, that no other mode of accounting for it existed. It is clear that innumerable causes might operate, in combination, to diminish the orbit, without even a possibility of our ever becoming acquainted with one of them. In the meantime, it has never been fairly shown, perhaps, why the retardation occasioned by the skirts of the Sun's atmosphere, through which the comet passes at perihelion, is not enough to account for the phænomenon. That Encke's comet will be absorbed into the Sun, is probable; that all the comets of the system will be absorbed, is more than merely possible; but, in such case, the principle of absorption must be referred to eccentricity or orbit—to the close approximation to the Sun, of the comets at their perihelia; and is a principle not affecting, in any degree, the ponderous *spheres*, which are to be regarded as the true material constituents of the Universe. Touching comets in general, let me here suggest, in passing, that we cannot be far wrong in looking upon them as the *lightning-flashes of the cosmical Heaven.*

The idea of retarding ether, and, through it, of a final agglomeration of all things, seemed at one time, however, to be confirmed by the observation of a positive decrease in the orbit of the solid moon. By reference to eclipses recorded 2500 years ago, it was found that the velocity of the satellite's revolution *then* was considerably less than it is *now;* that on the hypothesis that its motion in its orbit is uniformly in accordance with Kepler's law, and was accurately determined *then*—2500 years ago—it is now in advance of the position it *should* occupy, by nearly 9000 miles. The increase of velocity proved, of course, a diminution of orbit; and astronomers were fast yielding to a belief in an ether, as the sole mode of accounting for the phænomenon, when Lagrange came to the rescue. He showed that, owing to the configurations of the sphe-

roids, the shorter axes of their ellipses are subject to variation in length; the longer axes being permanent; and that this variation is continuous and vibratory—so that every orbit is in
a state of transition, either from circle to ellipse,
or from ellipse to circle. In the case of the moon,
where the shorter axis is *de*creasing, the orbit is
passing from circle to ellipse, and, consequently,
is *de*creasing too; but, after a long series of ages,
the ultimate eccentricity will be attained; then
the shorter axis will proceed to *in*crease, until the
orbit becomes a circle; when the process of short-
ening will again take place;—and so on forever.
In the case of the Earth, the orbit is passing
from ellipse to circle. The facts thus demonstrated do away, of course, with all necessity for
supposing an ether, and with all apprehension
of the system's instability—on the ether's account.

It will be remembered that I have myself assumed what we may term *an ether*. I have
spoken of a subtle *influence* which we know to be
ever in attendance upon matter, although becoming manifest only through matter's heterogeneity. To this *influence*—without daring to
touch it at all in any effort at explaining its
awful *nature*—I have referred the various phænomena of electricity, heat, light, magnetism;
and more—of vitality, consciousness, and
thought—in a word, of spirituality. It will be
seen, at once, then, that the ether thus conceived
is radically distinct from the ether of the astron-

omers; inasmuch as theirs is *matter* and mine *not*.

With the idea of material ether, seems, thus, to have departed altogether the thought of that universal agglomeration so long predetermined by the poetical fancy of mankind:—an agglomeration in which a sound Philosophy might have been warranted in putting faith, at least to a certain extent, if for no other reason than that by this poetical fancy it *had* been so predetermined. But so far as Astronomy—so far as mere Physics have yet spoken, the cycles of the Universe has no conceivable end. Had an end been demonstrated, however, from so purely collateral a cause as an ether, Man's instinct of the Divine *capacity to adapt,* would have rebelled against the demonstration. We should have been forced to regard the Universe with some such sense of dissatisfaction as we experience in contemplating an unnecessarily complex work of human art. Creation would have affected us as an imperfect *plot* in a romance, where the *dénouement* is awkwardly brought about by interposed incidents external and foreign to the main subject; instead of springing out of the bosom of the thesis—out of the heart of the ruling idea—instead of arising as a result of the primary proposition—as inseparable and inevitable part and parcel of the fundamental conception of the book.

What I mean by the symmetry of mere surface will now be more clearly understood. It is simply by the blandishment of this symmetry that we have been beguiled into the general idea of

IX. 10

which Mädler's hypothesis is but a part—the
idea of the vorticial indrawing of the orbs. Dismissing this nakedly physical conception, the
symmetry of principle sees the end of all things
metaphysically involved in the thought of a beginning; seeks and finds in this origin of all
things the *rudiment* of this end; and perceives
the impiety of supposing this end likely to be
brought about less simply—less directly—less
obviously—less artistically—than through *the reaction of the originating Act.*

Recurring, then, to a previous suggestion, let
us understand the systems—let us understand
each star, with its attendant planets—as but a
Titanic atom existing in space with precisely the
same inclination for Unity which characterized,
in the beginning, the actual atoms after their
irradiation throughout the Universal sphere. As
these original atoms rushed towards each other
in generally straight lines, so let us conceive as
at least generally rectilinear, the paths of the
system-atoms towards their respective centres of
aggregation:—and in this direct drawing together of the systems into clusters, with a similar and
simultaneous drawing together of the clusters
themselves while undergoing consolidation, we
have at length attained the great *Now*—the
awful Present—the Existing Condition of the
Universe.

Of the still more awful Future a not irrational
analogy may guide us in framing an hypothesis.
The equilibrium between the centripetal and centrifugal forces of each system, being necessarily

destroyed upon attainment of a certain proximity to the nucleus of the cluster to which it belongs, there must occur, at once, a chaotic or seemingly chaotic precipitation, of the moons upon the planets, of the planets upon the suns, and of the suns upon the nuclei; and the general result of this precipitation must be the gathering of the myriad now-existing stars of the firmament into an almost infinitely less number of almost infinitely superior spheres. In being immeasurably fewer, the worlds of that day will be immeasurably greater than our own. Then, indeed, amid unfathomable abysses, will be glaring unimaginable suns. But all this will be merely a climacic magnificence foreboding the great End. Of this End the new genesis described, can be but a very partial postponement. While undergoing consolidation, the clusters themselves, with a speed prodigiously accumulative, have been rushing towards their own general centre— and now, with a thousand-fold electric velocity, commensurate only with their material grandeur and with the spiritual passion of their appetite for oneness, the majestic remnants of the tribe of Stars flash, at length, into a common embrace. The inevitable catastrophe is at hand.

But this catastrophe—what is it? We have seen accomplished the ingathering of the orbs. Henceforward, are we not to understand *one material globe of globes* as constituting and comprehending the Universe? Such a fancy would be altogether at war with every assumption and consideration of this Discourse.

I have already alluded to that absolute *reciprocity of adaptation* which is the idiosyncrasy of the divine Art—stamping it divine. Up to this point of our reflections, we have been regarding the electrical influence as a something by dint of whose repulsion alone Matter is enabled to exist in that state of diffusion demanded for the fulfilment of its purposes:—so far, in a word, we have been considering the influence in question as ordained for Matter's sake to subserve the objects of matter. With a perfectly legitimate reciprocity, we are now permitted to look at Matter, as created *solely for the sake of this influence*—solely to serve the objects of this spiritual Ether. Through the aid—by the means—through the agency of Matter, and by dint of its heterogeneity—is this Ether manifested—is *Spirit individualized*. It is merely in the development of this Ether, through heterogeneity, that particular masses of Matter become animate—sensitive—and in the ratio of their heterogeneity;—some reaching a degree of sensitiveness involving what we call *Thought,* and thus attaining Conscious Intelligence.

In this view, we are enabled to perceive Matter as a Means—not as an End. Its purposes are thus seen to have been comprehended in its diffusion; and with the return into Unity these purposes cease. The absolutely consolidated globe of globes would be *objectless*—therefore not for a moment could it continue to exist. Matter, created for an end, would unquestionably, on fulfilment of that end, be Matter no longer. Let us

endeavor to understand that it would disappear,
and that God would remain all in all.

That every work of Divine conception must coexist and coexpire with its particular design,
seems to me especially obvious; and I make no
doubt that, on perceiving the final globe of globes
to be *objectless,* the majority of my readers will
be satisfied with my *"therefore* it cannot continue to exist." Nevertheless, as the startling
thought of its instantaneous disappearance is one
which the most powerful intellect cannot be expected readily to entertain on grounds so decidedly abstract, let us endeavor to look at the idea
from some other and more ordinary point of
view:—let us see how thoroughly and beautifully
it is corroborated in an *a posteriori* consideration
of Matter as we actually find it.

I have before said that "Attraction and Repulsion being undeniably the sole properties by
which Matter is manifested to Mind, we are justified in assuming that Matter *exists* only as Attraction and Repulsion—in other words that Attraction and Repulsion *are* Matter; there being
no conceivable case in which we may not employ
the term Matter and the terms 'Attraction' and
'Repulsion' taken together, as equivalent, and
therefore convertible, expressions of Logic."[*]

Now the very definition of Attraction implies
particularity—the existence of parts, particles, or
atoms, for we define it as the tendency of "each
atom, &c., to every other atom," &c., accord-

* Page 38—Paragraph commencing "Discarding now."

ing to a certain law. Of course where there are
no parts—where there is absolute Unity—where
the tendency to oneness is satisfied—there can
be no Attraction:—this has been fully shown,
and all Philosophy admits it. When, on fulfilment of its purposes, then, Matter shall have returned into its original condition of *One*—a condition which presupposes the expulsion of the
separative ether, whose province and whose capacity are limited to keeping the atoms apart until that great day when, this ether being no longer
needed, the overwhelming pressure of the finally
collective Attraction shall at length just sufficiently predominate* and expel it:—when, I say,
Matter, finally, expelling the Ether, shall have
returned into absolute Unity,—it will then (to
speak paradoxically for the moment) be Matter
without Attraction and without Repulsion—in
other words, Matter without Matter—in other
words, again, *Matter no more*. In sinking into
Unity, it will sink at once into that Nothingness
which, to all Finite Perception, Unity must be—
into that Material Nihility from which alone we
can conceive it to have been evoked—to have been
created by the Volition of God.

I repeat, then—Let us endeavor to comprehend that the final globe of globes will instan-
taneously disappear, and that God will remain
all in all.

But are we here to pause? Not so. On the
Universal agglomeration and dissolution, we can

---

* " Gravity, therefore, must be the strongest of forces."—
See page 42—Paragraph commencing, " Now to what."

readily conceive that a new and perhaps totally
different series of conditions may ensue—another
creation and irradiation, returning into itself—
another action and reaction of the Divine Will.
Guiding our imaginations by that omniprevalent
law of laws, the law of periodicity, are we not,
indeed, more than justified in entertaining a belief—let us say, rather, in indulging a hope—
that the processes we have here ventured to con-
template will be renewed forever, and forever,
and forever; a novel Universe swelling into existence, and then subsiding into nothingness, at
every throb of the Heart Divine?

And now—this Heart Divine—what is it? *It
is our own.*

Let not the merely seeming irreverence of this
idea frighten our souls from that cool exercise of
consciousness—from that deep tranquillity of
self-inspection—through which alone we can
hope to attain the presence of this, the most sublime of truths, and look it leisurely in the face.

The *phænomena* on which our conclusions
must at this point depend, are merely spiritual
shadows, but not the less thoroughly substantial.

We walk about, amid the destinies of our
world-existence, encompassed by dim but ever
present *Memories* of a Destiny more vast—very
distant in the by-gone time, and infinitely awful.

We live out a Youth peculiarly haunted by
such dreams; yet never mistaking them for
dreams. As Memories we *know* them. *During
our Youth* the distinction is too clear to deceive
us even for a moment.

So long as this Youth endures, the feeling *that we exist,* is the most natural of all feelings. We understand it *thoroughly.* That there was a period at which we did *not* exist—or, that it might so have happened that we never had existed at all—are the considerations, indeed, which *during this youth,* we find difficulty in understanding. Why we should *not* exist, is, *up to the epoch of our Manhood,* of all queries the most unanswerable. Existence—self-existence—existence from all Time and to all Eternity—seems, up to the epoch of Manhood, a normal and unquestionable condition:—*seems, because it is.*

But now comes the period at which a conventional World-Reason awakens us from the truth of our dream. Doubt, Surprise and Incomprehensibility arrive at the same moment. They say:—"You live, and the time was when you lived not. You have been created. An Intelligence exists greater than your own; and it is only through this Intelligence you live at all." These things we struggle to comprehend and cannot:—*cannot,* because these things, being untrue, are thus, of necessity, incomprehensible.

No thinking being lives who, at some luminous point of his life of thought, has not felt himself lost amid the surges of futile efforts at understanding or believing, that anything exists *greater than his own soul.* The utter impossibility of any one's soul feeling itself inferior to another; the intense, overwhelming dissatisfaction and rebellion at the thought:—these, with the omniprevalent aspirations at perfection, are but the spiritual, coincident with the material, struggles towards the original Unity—are, to my mind at least, a species of proof far surpassing what Man terms demonstration, that no one soul *is* inferior to another—that nothing is, or can be, superior to any one soul—that each soul is, in part, its own God—its own Creator:—in a word, that God—the material *and* spiritual God—*now* exists solely in the diffused Matter and Spirit of the Universe; and that the regathering of this diffused Matter and Spirit will be but the reconstitution of the *purely* Spiritual and Individual God.

In this view, and in this view alone, we comprehend the riddles of Divine Injustice—or Inexorable Fate. In this view alone the existence of Evil becomes intelligible; but in this view it becomes more—it becomes endurable. Our souls no longer rebel at a *Sorrow* which we ourselves have imposed upon ourselves, in furtherance of our own purposes—with a view—if even with a futile view—to the extension of our own *Joy*.

I have spoken of *Memories* that haunt us during our youth. They sometimes pursue us even in our Manhood:—assume gradually less and less indefinite shapes:—now and then speak to us with low voices, saying:

"There was an epoch in the Night of Time, when a still-existent Being existed—one of an absolutely infinite number of similar Beings that people the absolutely infinite domains of the ab-

solutely infinite space.* It was not and is not
in the power of this Being—any more than it is
in your own—to extend, by actual increase, the
joy of his Existence; but just as it *is* in your
power to expand or to concentrate your pleasures (the absolute amount of happiness remaining always the same) so did and does a similar
capability appertain to this Divine Being, who
thus passes his Eternity in perpetual variation of
Concentrated Self and almost Infinite Self-Dif-
fusion. What you call The Universe is but his
present expansive existence. He now feels his
life through an infinity of imperfect pleasures—
the partial and pain-intertangled pleasures of
those inconceivably numerous things which you
designate as his creatures, but which are really
but infinite individualizations of Himself. All
these creatures—*all*—those which you term animate, as well as those to whom you deny life for
no better reason than that you do not behold it
in operation—*all* these creatures have, in a
greater or less degree, a capacity for pleasure
and for pain:—*but the general sum of their sensations is precisely that amount of Happiness
which appertains by right to the Divine Being
when concentrated within Himself.* These creatures are all too, more or less conscious Intelligences; conscious, first, of a proper identity;
conscious, secondly, and by faint indeterminate
glimpses, of an identity with the Divine Being of
whom we speak—of an identity with God. Of

* See pages 110 and 111—Paragraph commencing " I reply
that the right," and ending " *proper and particular God.*"

the two classes of consciousness, fancy that the former will grow weaker, the latter stronger, during the long succession of ages which must elapse before these myriads of individual Intelligences become blended—when the bright stars become blended—into One.   Think that the sense of individual identity will be gradually merged in the general consciousness—that Man, for example, ceasing imperceptibly to feel himself Man, will at length attain that awfully triumphant epoch when he shall recognise his existence as that of Jehovah.   In the meantime bear in mind that all is Life—Life—Life within Life —the less within the greater, and all within the *Spirit Divine.*

THE POWER OF WORDS

[Published in the *Democratic Review*, June, 1845.]

Oinos.—Pardon, Agathos, the weakness of a spirit new-fledged with immortality!

Agathos.—You have spoken nothing, my Oinos, for which pardon is to be demanded. Not even here is knowledge a thing of intuition. For wisdom, ask of the angels freely, that it may be given!

Oinos.—But in this existence, I dreamed that I should be at once cognizant of all things, and thus at once happy in being cognizant of all.

Agathos.—Ah, not in knowledge is happiness, but in the acquisition of knowledge! In for ever knowing, we are for ever blessed; but to know all, were the curse of a fiend.

Oinos.—But does not The Most High know all?

Agathos.—*That* (since he is The Most Happy) must be still the *one* thing unknown even to Him.

Oinos.—But, since we grow hourly in knowledge, must not *at last* all things be known?

Agathos.—Look down into the abysmal distances!—attempt to force the gaze down the multitudinous vistas of the stars, as we sweep slowly through them thus—and thus—and thus! Even the spiritual vision, is it not at all points arrested by the continuous golden walls of the universe? —the walls of the myriads of the shining bodies that mere number has appeared to blend into unity?

Oinos.—I clearly perceive that the infinity of matter is no dream.

Agathos.—There are *no* dreams in Aidenn— but it is here whispered that, of this infinity of matter, the *sole* purpose is to afford infinite springs, at which the soul may allay the thirst *to know* which is for ever unquenchable within it— since to quench it, would be to extinguish the soul's self. Question me then, my Oinos, freely and without fear. Come! we will leave to the left the loud harmony of the Pleiades, and swoop outward from the throne into the starry meadows beyond Orion, where, for pansies and violets, and heart's-ease, are the beds of the triplicate and triple-tinted suns.

Oinos.—And now, Agathos, as we proceed, instruct me!—speak to me in the earth's familiar tones! I understood not what you hinted to me, just now, of the modes or of the methods of what, during mortality, we were accustomed to call Creation. Do you mean to say that the Creator is not God?

Agathos.—I mean to say that the Deity does not create.

Oinos.—Explain!

Agathos.—In the beginning *only,* he created.

The seeming creatures which are now, throughout the universe, so perpetually springing into being, can only be considered as the mediate or indirect, not as the direct or immediate results of the Divine creative power.

Oinos.—Among men, my Agathos, this idea would be considered heretical in the extreme.

Agathos.—Among angels, my Oinos, it is seen to be simply true.

Oinos.—I can comprehend you thus far—that certain operations of what we term Nature, or the natural laws, will, under certain conditions, give rise to that which has all the *appearance* of creation. Shortly before the final overthrow of the earth, there were, I well remember, many very successful experiments in what some philosophers were weak enough to denominate the creation of animalculæ.

Agathos.—The cases of which you speak were, in fact, instances of the secondary creation—and of the *only* species of creation which has ever been, since the first word spoke into existence the first law.

Oinos.—Are not the starry worlds that, from the abyss of nonentity, burst hourly forth into the heavens—are not these stars, Agathos, the immediate handiwork of the King?

Agathos.—Let me endeavor, my Oinos, to lead you, step by step, to the conception I intend. You are well aware that, as no thought can perish, so no act is without infinite result. We moved our hands, for example, when we were dwellers on the earth, and, in so doing, we gave vibration to the atmosphere which engirdled it. This vibration was indefinitely extended, till it gave impulse to every particle of the earth's air, which thenceforward, *and for ever,* was actuated by the one movement of the hand. This fact the mathematicians of our globe well knew. They made the special effects, indeed, wrought in the fluid by special impulses, the subject of exact calculation—so that it became easy to determine in what precise period an impulse of given extent would engirdle the orb, and impress (for ever) every atom of the atmosphere circumambient. Retrograding, they found no difficulty, from a given effect, under given conditions, in determining the value of the original impulse. Now the mathematicians who saw that the results of any given impulse were absolutely endless—and who saw that a portion of these results were accurately traceable through the agency of algebraic analysis—who saw, too, the facility of the retrogradation—these men saw, at the same time, that this species of analysis itself, had within itself a capacity for indefinite progress—that there were no bounds conceivable to its advancement and applicability, except within the intellect of him who advanced or applied it. But at this point our mathematicians paused.

Oinos.—And why, Agathos, should they have proceeded?

Agathos.—Because there were some considerations of deep interest beyond. It was deducible from what they knew, that to a being of infinite understanding—one to whom the *perfection* of the algebraic analysis lay unfolded—there could be no difficulty in tracing every impulse given the air—and the ether through the air—to the remotest consequences at any even infinitely remote epoch of time. It is indeed demonstrable that every such impulse *given the air,* must, *in the end,* impress every individual thing that exists *within the universe;*—and the being of infinite understanding—the being whom we have imagined—might trace the remote undulations of the impulse—trace them upward and onward in their influences upon all particles of all matter —upward and onward for ever in their modifications of old forms—or, in other words, *in their creation of new*—until he found them reflected— unimpressive *at last*—back from the throne of the Godhead. And not only could such a being do this, but at any epoch, should a given result be afforded him—should one of these numberless comets, for example, be presented to his inspection—he could have no difficulty in determining, by the analytic retrogradation, to what original impulse was due. This power of retrogradation in its absolute fulness and perfection—this faculty of referring at *all* epochs, *all* effects to *all* causes—is of course the prerogative of the Deity alone—but in every variety of degree, short of the absolute perfection, is the power itself exercised by the whole host of the Angelic Intelligences.

Oinos.—But you speak merely of impulses upon the air.

Agathos.—In speaking of the air, I referred

only to the earth: but the general proposition has reference to impulses upon the ether—which, since it pervades, and alone pervades all space, is thus the great medium of *creation*.

Oinos.—Then all motion, of whatever nature, creates?

Agathos.—It must: but a true philosophy has long taught that the source of all motion is thought—and the source of all thought is——

Oinos.—God.

Agathos.—I have spoken to you, Oinos, as to a child of the fair Earth which lately perished—of impulses upon the atmosphere of the Earth.

Oinos.—You did.

Agathos.—And while I thus spoke, did there not cross your mind some thought of the *physical power of words?* Is not every word an impulse on the air?

Oinos.—But why, Agathos, do you weep—and why, oh, why do your wings droop as we hover above this fair star—which is the greenest and yet most terrible of all we have encountered in our flight? Its brilliant flowers look like a fairy dream—but its fierce volcanoes like the passions of a turbulent heart.

Agathos.—They *are!*—they *are!* This wild star—it is now three centuries since, with clasped hands, and with streaming eyes, at the feet of my beloved—I spoke it—with a few passionate sentences—into birth. Its brilliant flowers *are* the dearest of all unfulfilled dreams, and its raging volcanoes *are* the passions of the most turbulent and unhallowed of hearts.

IX. 11

THE COLLOQUY OF MONOS AND UNA.

[Published in *Graham's Magazine*, August, 1841.]

Μέλλοντα ταῦτα.

Sophocles—Antig:
These things are in the future.

Una.—"Born again?"

Monos.—Yes, fairest and best beloved Una, "born again." These were the words upon whose mystical meaning I had so long pondered, rejecting the explanations of the priesthood, until Death himself resolved for me the secret.

Una.—Death!

Monos.—How strangely, sweet Una, you echo my words! I observe, too, a vacillation in your step—a joyous inquietude in your eyes. You are confused and oppressed by the majestic novelty of the Life Eternal. Yes, it was of Death I spoke. And here how singularly sounds that word which of old was wont to bring terror to all hearts—throwing a mildew upon all pleasures!

Una.—Ah, Death, the spectre which sate at all feasts! How often, Monos, did we lose ourselves in speculations upon its nature! How mysteriously did it act as a check to human bliss—saying unto it "thus far, and no farther!" That earnest mutual love, my own Monos, which burned within our bosoms—how vainly did we flatter ourselves, feeling happy in its first up-springing, that our happiness would strengthen with its strength! Alas! as it grew, so grew in our hearts the dread of that evil hour which was hurrying to separate us forever! Thus, in time, it became painful to love. Hate would have been mercy then.

Monos.—Speak not here of these griefs, dear Una—mine, mine forever now!

Una.—But the memory of past sorrow—is it not present joy? I have much to say yet of the things which have been. Above all, I burn to know the incidents of your own passage through the dark Valley and Shadow.

Monos.—And when did the radiant Una ask anything of her Monos in vain? I will be minute in relating all—but at what point shall the weird narrative begin?

Una.—At what point?

Monos.—You have said.

Una.—Monos, I comprehend you. In Death we have both learned the propensity of man to define the indefinable. I will not say, then, commence with the moment of life's cessation—but commence with that sad, sad instant when, the fever having abandoned you, you sank into a breathless and motionless torpor, and I pressed down your pallid eyelids with the passionate fingers of love.

Monos.—One word first, my Una, in regard to man's general condition at this epoch. You will remember that one or two of the wise among our forefathers—wise in fact, although not in the world's esteem—had ventured to doubt the propriety of the term "improvement," as applied to the progress of our civilization. There were periods in each of the five or six centuries immediately preceding our dissolution, when arose some vigorous intellect, boldly contending for those principles whose truth appears now, to our disenfranchised reason, so utterly obvious—principles which should have taught our race to submit to the guidance of the natural laws, rather than attempt their control. At long intervals some master-minds appeared, looking upon each advance in practical science as a retro-gradation in the true utility. Occasionally the poetic intellect—that intellect which we now feel to have been the most exalted of all—since those truths which to us were of the most enduring importance could only be reached by that *analogy* which speaks in proof-tones to the imagination alone, and to the unaided reason bears no weight—occasionally did this poetic intellect proceed a step farther in the evolving of the vague idea of the philosophic, and find in the mystic parable that tells of the tree of knowledge, and of its forbidden fruit, death-producing, a distinct intimation that knowledge was not meet for man in the infant condition of his soul. And these men—the poets—living and perishing amid the scorn of the "utilitarians"—of rough pedants, who arrogated to themselves a title which could have been properly applied only to the scorned—these men, the poets, pondered piningly, yet not unwisely, upon the ancient days when our wants were not more simple than our enjoyments were keen— days when *mirth* was a word unknown, so solemnly deep-toned was happiness—holy, august and blissful days, when blue rivers ran undammed, between hills unhewn, into far forest solitudes, primæval, odorous, and unexplored.

Yet these noble exceptions from the general misrule served but to strengthen it by opposition. Alas! we had fallen upon the most evil of all our evil days. The great "movement"—that was the cant term—went on: a diseased commotion, moral and physical. Art—the Arts—arose supreme, and, once enthroned, cast chains upon the intellect which had elevated them to power. Man, because he could not but acknowledge the majesty of Nature, fell into childish exultation at his acquired and still-increasing dominion over her elements. Even while he stalked a God in his own fancy, an infantine imbecility came over him. As might be supposed from the origin of his disorder, he grew infected with system, and with abstraction. He enwrapped himself in generalities. Among other odd ideas, that of universal equality gained ground; and in the face of analogy and of God—in despite of the loud warning voice of the laws of *gradation* so visibly pervading all things in Earth and Heaven—wild attempts at an omni-prevalent Democracy were made. Yet this evil sprang

necessarily from the leading evil, Knowledge.
Man could not both know and succumb. Meantime huge smoking cities arose, innumerable.
Green leaves shrank before the hot breath of fur-
naces. The fair face of Nature was deformed as
with the ravages of some loathsome disease. And
methinks, sweet Una, even our slumbering sense
of the forced and of the far-fetched might have
arrested us here. But now it appears that we had
worked out our own destruction in the perversion
of our *taste*, or rather in the blind neglect of its
culture in the schools. For, in truth, it was at
this crisis that taste alone—that faculty which,
holding a middle position between the pure intellect and the moral sense, could never safely have
been disregarded—it was now that taste alone
could have led us gently back to Beauty, to Nature, and to Life. But alas for the pure contem-
plative spirit and majestic intuition of Plato!
Alas for the μουσική which he justly regarded
as an all-sufficient education for the soul! Alas
for him and for it!—since both were most des-
perately needed when both were most entirely
forgotten or despised.*

* " It will be hard to discover a better [method of education]
than that which the experience of so many ages has already
discovered; and this may be summed up as consisting in
gymnastics for the body, and *music* for the soul."—Repub. lib.
2. "For this reason is a musical education most essential;
since it causes Rhythm and Harmony to Penetrate most in-
timately into the soul, taking the strongest hold upon it, filling it with *beauty* and making the man *beautiful-minded.*
. . . . He will praise and admire *the beautiful;* will receive it with joy into his soul, will feed upon it, and *assimi-
late his own condition with it.*"—Ibid. lib. 3. Music (μουσική)
had, however, among the Athenians, a far more comprehensive
signification than with us. It included not only the harmonies

Pascal, a philosopher whom we both love, has said, how truly!—"*que tout notre raisonnement se rèduit à céder au sentiment;*" and it is not impossible that the sentiment of the natural, had time permitted it, would have regained its old ascendancy over the harsh mathematical reason of the schools. But this thing was not to be. Prematurely induced by intemperance of knowledge, the old age of the world drew on. This the mass of mankind saw not, or, living lustily although unhappily, affected not to see. But, for myself, the Earth's records had taught me to look for widest ruin as the price of highest civilization. I had imbibed a prescience of our Fate from comparison of China the simple and enduring, with Assyria the architect, with Egypt the astrologer, with Nubia, more crafty than either, the turbulent mother of all Arts. In history† of these regions I met with a ray from the Future. The individual artificialities of the three latter were local diseases of the Earth, and in their individual overthrows we had seen local remedies applied; but for the infected world at large I could anticipate no regeneration save in death. That man, as a race, should not become extinct, I saw that he must be "*born again.*"

And now it was, fairest and dearest, that we wrapped our spirits, daily, in dreams. Now it

of time and of tune, but the poetic diction, sentiment and creation, each in its widest sense. The study of *music* was with them, in fact, the general cultivation of the taste—of that which recognizes the beautiful—in contra-distinction from reason, which deals only with the true.

† "History," from ἱστορεῖν, to contemplate.

was that, in twilight, we discoursed of the days to come, when the Art-scarred surface of the Earth, having undergone that purification* which alone could efface its rectangular obscenities, should clothe itself anew in the verdure and the mountain-slopes and the smiling waters of Paradise, and be rendered at length a fit dwelling-place for man:—for man the Death-purged—for man to whose now exalted intellect there should be poison in knowledge no more—for the redeemed, regenerated, blissful, and now immortal, but still for the *material*, man.

Una.—Well do I remember these conversations, dear Monos; but the epoch of the fiery overthrow was not so near at hand as we believed, and as the corruption you indicate did surely warrant us in believing. Men lived; and died individually. You yourself sickened, and passed into the grave; and thither your constant Una speedily followed you. And though the century which has since elapsed, and whose conclusion brings us thus together once more, tortured our slumbering senses with no impatience of duration, yet, my Monos, it was a century still.

Monos.—Say, rather, a point in the vague infinity. Unquestionably, it was in the Earth's dotage that I died. Wearied at heart with anxieties which had their origin in the general turmoil and decay, I succumbed to the fierce fever. After some few days of pain, and many of dreamy delirium replete with ecstasy, the

---

* The word " *purification* " seems here to be used with reference to its root in the Greek πῦρ, fire.

manifestations of which you mistook for pain, while I longed but was impotent to undeceive you—after some days there came upon me, as you have said, a breathless and motionless torpor; and this was termed *Death* by those who stood around me.

Words are vague things. My condition did not deprive me of sentience. It appeared to me not greatly dissimilar to the extreme quiescence of him, who, having slumbered long and profoundly, lying motionless and fully prostrate in a midsummer noon, begins to steal slowly back into consciousness, through the mere sufficiency of his sleep, and without being awakened by external disturbances.

I breathed no longer. The pulses were still. The heart had ceased to beat. Volition had not departed, but was powerless. The senses were unusually active, although eccentrically so—assuming often each other's functions at random. The taste and the smell were inextricably confounded, and became one sentiment, abnormal and intense. The rose-water with which your tenderness had moistened my lips to the last, affected me with sweet fancies of flowers—fantastic flowers, far more lovely than any of the old Earth, but whose prototypes we have here blooming around us. The eyelids, transparent and bloodless, offered no complete impediment to vision. As volition was in abeyance, the balls could not roll in their sockets—but all objects within the range of the visual hemisphere were seen with more or less distinctness; the rays which fell upon the external retina, or into the corner of the eye, producing a more vivid effect than those which struck the front or interior surface. Yet, in the former instance, this effect was so far anomalous that I appreciated it only as *sound*—sound sweet or discordant as the matters presenting themselves at my side were light or dark in shade—curved or angular in outline. The hearing, at the same time, although excited in degree, was not irregular in action—estimating real sounds with an extravagance of precision, not less than of sensibility. Touch had undergone a modification more peculiar. Its impressions were tardily received, but pertinaciously retained, and resulted always in the highest physical pleasure. Thus the pressure of your sweet fingers upon my eyelids, at first only recognised through vision, at length, long after their removal, filled my whole being with a sensual delight immeasurable. I say with a sensual delight. *All* my perceptions were purely sensual. The materials furnished the passive brain by the senses were not in the least degree wrought into shape by the deceased understanding. Of pain there was some little; of pleasure there was much; but of moral pain or pleasure none at all. Thus your wild sobs floated into my ear with all their mournful cadences, and were appreciated in their every variation of sad tone; but they were soft musical sounds and no more; they conveyed to the extinct reason no intimation of the sorrows which gave them birth; while the large and constant tears which fell upon my face, telling the bystanders of a heart which broke, thrilled every fibre of my frame with ecstasy alone. And this was in truth the *Death* of which these bystanders spoke reverently, in low whispers—you, sweet Una, gaspingly, with loud cries.

They attired me for the coffin—three or four dark figures which flitted busily to and fro. As these crossed the direct line of my vision they affected me as *forms;* but upon passing to my side their images impressed me with the idea of shrieks, groans, and other dismal expressions of terror, of horror, or of woe. You alone, habited in a white robe, passed in all directions musically about me.

The day waned; and, as its light faded away, I became possessed by a vague uneasiness—an anxiety such as the sleeper feels when sad real sounds fall continuously within his ear—low distant bell-tones, solemn, at long but equal intervals, and commingling with melancholy dreams. Night arrived; and with its shadows a heavy discomfort. It oppressed my limbs with the oppression of some dull weight, and was palpable. There was also a moaning sound, not unlike the distant reverberation of surf, but more continuous, which, beginning with the first twilight, had grown in strength with the darkness. Suddenly lights were brought into the room, and this reverberation became forthwith interrupted into frequent unequal bursts of the same sound, but less dreary and less distinct. The ponderous oppression was in a great measure relieved; and,

issuing from the flame of each lamp, (for there
were many,) there flowed unbrokenly into my
ears a strain of melodious monotone. And when
now, dear Una, approaching the bed upon which
I lay outstretched, you sat gently by my side,
breathing odor from your sweet lips, and press-
ing them upon my brow, there arose tremulously
within my bosom, and mingling with the merely
physical sensations which circumstances had
called forth, a something akin to sentiment itself
—a feeling that, half appreciating, half re-
sponded to your earnest love and sorrow; but
this feeling took no root in the pulseless heart,
and seemed indeed rather a shadow than a reality, and faded quickly away, first into extreme
quiescence, and then into a purely sensual pleasure as before.

And now, from the wreck and the chaos of
the usual senses, there appeared to have arisen
within me a sixth, all perfect. In its exercise
I found a wild delight—yet a delight still physical, inasmuch as the understanding had in it
no part. Motion in the animal frame had fully
ceased. No muscle quivered; no nerve thrilled;
no artery throbbed. But there seemed to have
sprung up in the brain, *that* of which no words
could convey to the merely human intelligence
even an indistinct conception. Let me term it
a mental pendulous pulsation. It was the moral
embodiment of man's abstract idea of *Time*. By
the absolute equalization of this movement—or
of such as this—had the cycles of the firmamental orbs themselves, been adjusted. By its aid

I measured the irregularities of the clock upon
the mantel, and of the watches of the attendants.
Their tickings came sonorously to my ears. The
slightest deviations from the true proportion—
and these deviations were omni-prævalent—affected me just as violations of abstract truth
were wont, on earth, to affect the moral sense.
Although no two of the time-pieces in the chamber struck the individual seconds accurately together, yet I had no difficulty in holding steadily
in mind the tones, and the respective momentary
errors of each. And this—this keen, perfect,
self-existing sentiment of *duration*—this sentiment existing (as man could not possibly have
conceived it to exist) independently of any succession of events—this idea—this sixth sense,
upspringing from the ashes of the rest, was the
first obvious and certain step of the intemporal
soul upon the threshold of the temporal Eternity.

It was midnight; and you still sat by my
side. All others had departed from the chamber
of Death. They had deposited me in the coffin.
The lamps burned flickeringly; for this I knew
by the tremulousness of the monotonous strains.
But, suddenly, these strains diminished in distinctness and in volume. Finally they ceased.
The perfume in my nostrils died away. Forms
affected my vision no longer. The oppression of
the Darkness uplifted itself from my bosom. A
dull shock like that of electricity pervaded my
frame, and was followed by total loss of the idea
of contact. All of what man has termed sense
was merged in the sole consciousness of entity,

and in the one abiding sentiment of duration. The mortal body had been at length stricken with the hand of the deadly *Decay*.

Yet had not all of sentience departed; for the consciousness and the sentiment remaining supplied some of its functions by a lethargic intuition. I appreciated the direful change now in operation upon the flesh, and, as the dreamer is sometimes aware of the bodily presence of one who leans over him, so, sweet Una, I still dully felt that you sat by my side. So, too, when the noon of the second day came, I was not unconscious of those movements which displaced you from my side, which confined me within the coffin, which deposited me within the hearse, which bore me to the grave, which lowered me within it, which heaped heavily the mould upon me, and which thus left me, in blackness and corruption, to my sad and solemn slumbers with the worm.

And here, in the prison-house which has few secrets to disclose, there rolled away days and weeks and months; and the soul watched narrowly each second as it flew, and, without effort, took record of its flight—without effort and without object.

A year passed. The consciousness of *being* had grown hourly more indistinct, and that of mere *locality* had, in great measure, usurped its position. The idea of entity was becoming merged in that of *place*. The narrow space immediately surrounding what had been the body, was now growing to be the body itself. At length, as often happens to the sleeper (by sleep and its world alone is *Death* imaged)—at length, as sometimes happened on Earth to the deep slumberer, when some fitting light half startled him into awaking, yet left him half enveloped in dreams—so to me, in the strict embrace of the *Shadow*, came *that* light which alone might have had power to startle—the light of enduring *Love*. Men toiled at the grave in which I lay darkling. They upthrew the damp earth. Upon my mouldering bones there descended the coffin of Una.

And now again all was void. That nebulous light had been extinguished. That feeble thrill had vibrated itself into quiescence. Many *lustra* had supervened. Dust had returned to dust. The worm had food no more. The sense of being had at length utterly departed, and there reigned in its stead—instead of all things—dominant and perpetual—the autocrats *Place* and *Time*. For *that* which *was not*—for that which had no form —for that which had no thought—for that which had no sentience—for that which was soulless, yet of which matter formed no portion—for all this nothingness, yet for all this immortality, the grave was still a home, and the corrosive hours, co-mates.

THE CONVERSATION OF EIROS AND CHARMION

[Published in *Burton's Gentleman's Magazine*, December, 1839.]

Πῦρ σοι προσοίσω·

I will bring fire to thee.
Euripides—Androm:

EIROS.

WHY do you call me Eiros?

CHARMION.

So henceforward will you always be called. You must forget, too, *my* earthly name. and speak to me as Charmion.

EIROS.

This is indeed no dream!

CHARMION.

Dreams are with us no more;—but of these mysteries anon. I rejoice to see you looking life-like and rational. The film of the shadow has already passed from off your eyes. Be of heart, and fear nothing, Your allotted days of stupor have expired; and, to-morrow, I will myself induct you into the full joys and wonders of your novel existence.

EIROS.

True—I feel no stupor—none at all. The wild sickness and the terrible darkness have left me, and I hear no longer that mad, rushing, horrible sound, like the "voice of many waters." Yet my senses are bewildered, Charmion, with the keenness of their perception of *the new*.

CHARMION.

A few days will remove all this;—but I fully understand you, and feel for you. It is now ten earthly years since I underwent what you undergo—yet the remembrance of it hangs by me still. You have now suffered all of pain, however, which you will suffer in Aidenn.

EIROS.

In Aidenn?

CHARMION.

In Aidenn.

EIROS.

Oh God!—pity me, Charmion!—I am overburthened with the majesty of all things—of the unknown now known—of the speculative Future merged in the august and certain Present.

IX. 12

CHARMION.

Grapple not now with such thoughts. To-morrow we will speak of this. Your mind wavers, and its agitation will find relief in the exercise of simple memories. Look not around, nor forward—but back. I am burning with anxiety to hear the details of that stupendous event which threw you among us. Tell me of it. Let us converse of familiar things, in the old familiar language of the world which has so fearfully perished.

EIROS.

Most fearfully, fearfully!—this is indeed no dream.

CHARMION.

Dreams are no more. Was I much mourned, my Eiros?

EIROS.

Mourned, Charmion?—oh deeply. To that last hour of all, there hung a cloud of intense gloom and devout sorrow over your household.

CHARMION.

And that last hour—speak of it. Remember that, beyond the naked fact of the catastrophe itself, I know nothing. When, coming out from among mankind, I passed into Night through the Grave—at that period, if I remember aright, the calamity which overwhelmed you was utterly

unanticipated. But, indeed, I knew little of the
speculative philosophy of the day.

EIROS.

The individual calamity was, as you say, entirely unanticipated; but analogous misfortunes
had been long a subject of discussion with astronomers. I need scarce tell you, my friend,
that, even when you left us, men had agreed to
understand those passages in the most holy writ-
ings which speak of the final destruction of all
things by fire, as having reference to the orb of
the earth alone. But in regard to the immediate agency of the ruin, speculation had been at
fault from that epoch in astronomical knowledge
in which the comets were divested of the terrors
of flame. The very moderate density of these
bodies had been well established. They had
been observed to pass among the satellites of
Jupiter, without bringing about any sensible alteration either in the masses or in the orbits of
these secondary planets. We had long regarded
the wanderers as vapory creations of inconceivable tenuity, and as altogether incapable of doing injury to our substantial globe, even in the
event of contact. But contact was not in any
degree dreaded; for the elements of all the
comets were accurately known. That among
them we should look for the agency of the threat-
ened fiery destruction had been for many years
considered an inadmissible idea. But wonders
and wild fancies had been, of late days, strangely
rife among mankind; and, although it was only

with a few of the ignorant that actual apprehension prevailed, upon the announcement by astronomers of a *new* comet, yet this announcement was generally received with I know not what of agitation and mistrust.

The elements of the strange orb were immediately calculated, and it was at once conceded by all observers, that its path, at perihelion, would bring it into very close proximity with the earth. There were two or three astronomers, of secondary note, who resolutely maintained that a contact was inevitable. I cannot very well express to you the effect of this intelligence upon the people. For a few short days they would not believe an assertion which their intellect, so long employed among worldly considerations, could not in any manner grasp. But the truth of a vitally important fact soon makes its way into the understanding of even the most stolid. Finally, all men saw that astronomical knowledge lied not, and they awaited the comet. Its approach was not, at first, seemingly rapid; nor was its appearance of very unusual character. It was of a dull red, and had little perceptible train. For seven or eight days we saw no material increase in its apparent diameter, and but a partial alteration in its color. Meantime, the ordinary affairs of men were discarded, and all interests absorbed in a growing discussion, instituted by the philosophic, in respect to the cometary nature. Even the grossly ignorant aroused their sluggish capacities to such considerations. The learned *now* gave their intellect—their soul

—to no such points as the allaying of fear, or to the sustenance of loved theory. They sought— they panted for right views. They groaned for perfected knowledge. *Truth* arose in the purity of her strength and exceeding majesty, and the wise bowed down and adored.

That material injury to our globe or to its inhabitants would result from the apprehended contact, was an opinion which hourly lost ground among the wise; and the wise were now freely permitted to rule the reason and the fancy of the crowd. It was demonstrated, that the density of the comet's *nucleus* was far less than that of our rarest gas; and the harmless passage of a similar visitor among the satellites of Jupiter was a point strongly insisted upon, and which served greatly to allay terror. Theologists, with an earnestness fear-enkindled, dwelt upon the biblical prophecies, and expounded them to the people with a directness and simplicity of which no previous instance had been known. That the final destruction of the earth must be brought about by the agency of fire, was urged with a spirit that enforced every where conviction; and that the comets were of no fiery nature (as all men now knew) was a truth which relieved all, in a great measure, from the apprehension of the great calamity foretold. It is noticeable that the popular prejudices and vulgar errors in regard to pestilences and wars—errors which were wont to prevail upon every appearance of a comet— were now altogether unknown. As if by some sudden convulsive exertion, reason had at once hurled superstition from her throne. The feeblest intellect had derived vigor from excessive interest.

What minor evils might arise from the contact were points of elaborate question. The learned spoke of slight geological disturbances, of probable alterations in climate, and consequently in vegetation; of possible magnetic and electric influences. Many held that no visible or perceptible effect would in any manner be produced. While such discussions were going on, their subject gradually approached, growing larger in apparent diameter, and of a more brilliant lustre. Mankind grew paler as it came. All human operations were suspended.

There was an epoch in the course of the general sentiment when the comet had attained, at length, a size surpassing that of any previously recorded visitation. The people now, dismissing any lingering hope that the astronomers were wrong, experienced all the certainty of evil. The chimerical aspect of their terror was gone. The hearts of the stoutest of our race beat violently within their bosoms. A very few days sufficed, however, to merge even such feelings in sentiments more unendurable. We could no longer apply to the strange orb any *accustomed* thoughts. Its *historical* attributes had disappeared. It oppressed us with a hideous *novelty* of emotion. We saw it not as an astronomical phenomenon in the heavens, but as an incubus upon our hearts, and a shadow upon our brains. It had taken, with inconceivable rapidity, the character of a gigantic mantle of rare flame, extending from horizon to horizon.

Yet a day, and men breathed with greater freedom. It was clear that we were already within the influence of the comet; yet we lived. We even felt an unusual elasticity of frame and vivacity of mind. The exceeding tenuity of the object of our dread was apparent; for all heavenly objects were plainly visible through it. Meantime, our vegetation had perceptibly altered; and we gained faith, from this predicted circumstance, in the foresight of the wise. A wild luxuriance of foliage, utterly unknown before, burst out upon every vegetable thing.

Yet another day—and the evil was not altogether upon us. It was now evident that its nucleus would first reach us. A wild change had come over all men; and the first sense of pain was the wild signal for general lamentation and horror. This first sense of pain lay in a rigorous constriction of the breast and lungs, and an insufferable dryness of the skin. It could not be denied that our atmosphere was radically affected; the conformation of this atmosphere and the possible modifications to which it might be subjected, were now the topics of discussion. The result of investigation sent an electric thrill of the intensest terror through the universal heart of man.

It had been long known that the air which encircled us was a compound of oxygen and nitrogen gases, in the proportion of twenty-one measures of oxygen, and seventy-nine of nitrogen, in every one hundred of the atmosphere. Oxygen, which was the principle of combustion, and the vehicle of heat, was absolutely necessary to the support of animal life, and was the most powerful and energetic agent in nature. Nitrogen, on the contrary, was incapable of supporting either animal life or flame. An unnatural excess of oxygen would result, it had been ascertained, in just such an elevation of the animal spirits as we had latterly experienced. It was the pursuit, the extension of the idea, which had engendered awe. What would be the result of *a total extraction of the nitrogen?* A combustion irresistible, all-devouring, omni-prevalent, immediate;—the entire fulfilment, in all their minute and terrible details, of the fiery and horror-inspiring denunciations of the prophecies of the Holy Book.

Why need I paint, Charmion, the now disenchained frenzy of mankind? That tenuity in the comet which had previously inspired us with hope, was now the source of the bitterness of despair. In its impalpable gaseous character we clearly perceived the consummation of Fate. Meantime a day again passed—bearing away with it the last shadow of Hope. We gasped in the rapid modification of the air. The red blood bounded tumultuously through its strict channels. A furious delirium possessed all men; and, with arms rigidly outstretched towards the threatening heavens, they trembled and shrieked aloud. But the nucleus of the destroyer was now upon us;—even here in Aidenn, I shudder while I speak. Let me be brief—brief as the ruin that

overwhelmed. For a moment there was a wild
lurid light alone, visiting and penetrating all
things. Then—let us bow down, Charmion, before the excessive majesty of the great God!—
then, there came a shouting and pervading
sound, as if from the mouth itself of HIM; while
the whole incumbent mass of ether in which we
existed, burst at once into a species of intense
flame, for whose surpassing brilliancy and all-
fervid heat even the angels in the high Heaven
of pure knowledge have no name. Thus ended
all.

THE PHILOSOPHY OF FURNITURE

[Published in *Burton's Gentleman's Magazine*, May, 1840.]

IN the internal decoration, if not in the external architecture of their residences, the English are supreme. The Italians have but little sentiment beyond marbles and colors. In France, *meliora probant, deteriora sequuntur*— the people are too much a race of gad-abouts to maintain those beautiful proprieties of which, indeed, they have a delicate appreciation, or at least the elements of a proper sense. The Chinese and most of the Eastern races have a warm but inappropriate fancy. The Scotch are *poor* decorists. The Dutch have, perhaps, an indeterminate idea that a curtain is not a cabbage. In Spain they are *all* curtains—a nation of hangmen. The Russians do not furnish. The Hottentots and Kickapoos are very well in their way. The Yankees alone are preposterous.

How this happens, it is not difficult to see. We have no aristocracy of blood, and having therefore as a natural, and indeed as an inevitable thing, fashioned for ourselves an aristocracy of dollars, the *display of wealth* has here to take the place and perform the office of the heraldic display in monarchial countries. By a transition readily understood, and which might have been as readily foreseen, we have been brought to merge in simple *show* our notions of taste itself.

To speak less abstractedly. In England, for example, no mere parade of costly appurtenances would be so likely, as with us, to create an impression of the beautiful in respect to the appurtenances themselves—or to taste as regards the proprietor:—this for the reason, first, that wealth is not, in England, the loftiest object of ambition as constituting a nobility; and, secondly, that there, the true nobility of blood, confining itself within the strict limits of legitimate taste, rather avoids than affects that mere costliness in which a *parvenu* rivalry may at any time be successfully attempted. The people *will* imitate the nobles, and the result is a thorough diffusion of the proper feeling. But in America, the coins current being the sole arms of the aristocracy, their display may be said, in general, to be the sole means of aristocratic distinction; and the populace, looking always upward for models, are insensibly led to confound the two entirely separate ideas of magnificence and beauty. In short, the cost of an article of furniture has at length come to be, with us, nearly the sole test of its merit in a decorative point of view—and this test, once established, has led the way to many analogous errors, readily traceable to the one primitive folly.

There could be nothing more directly offensive to the eye of an artist than the interior of what is termed in the United States—that is to say, in Appallachia—a well-furnished apartment. Its most usual defect is a want of keeping. We speak of the keeping of a room as we would of the keeping of a picture—for both the picture and the room are amenable to those undeviating principles which regulate all varieties of art; and very nearly the same laws by which we decide on the higher merits of a painting, suffice for decision on the adjustment of a chamber.

A want of keeping is observable sometimes in the character of the several pieces of furniture, but generally in their colors or modes of adaptation to use. *Very* often the eye is offended by their inartistical arrangement. Straight lines are too prevalent—too uninterruptedly continued—or clumsily interrupted at right angles. If curved lines occur, they are repeated into unpleasant uniformity. By undue precision, the appearance of many a fine apartment is utterly spoiled.

Curtains are rarely well disposed, or well chosen, in respect to other decorations. With formal furniture, curtains are out of place; and an extensive volume of drapery of any kind is, under any circumstances, irreconcilable with good taste—the proper quantum, as well as the proper adjustment, depending upon the character of the general effect.

Carpets are better understood of late than of

ancient days, but we still very frequently err in
their patterns and colors. The soul of the apartment is the carpet. From it are deduced not
only the hues but the forms of all objects incumbent. A judge at common law may be an ordinary man; a good judge of a carpet *must be*
a genius. Yet we have heard discoursing of carpets, with the air *"d'un mouton qui rêve,"* fel-
lows who should not and who could not be en-
trusted with the management of their own
moustaches. Every one knows that a large floor
may have a covering of large figures, and that a
small one *must* have a covering of small—yet
this is not all the knowledge in the world. As
regards texture, the Saxony is alone admissible.
Brussels is the preter-pluperfect tense of fashion, and Turkey is taste in its dying agonies.
Touching pattern—a carpet should *not* be be-
dizzened out like a Riccaree Indian—all red
chalk, yellow ochre, and cock's feathers. In
brief—distinct grounds, and vivid circular or
cycloid figures, *of no meaning,* are here Median
laws. The abomination of flowers, or represen-
tations of well-known objects of any kind, should
not be endured within the limits of Christendom.
Indeed, whether on carpets, or curtains, or tapes-
try, or ottoman coverings, all upholstery of this
nature should be rigidly Arabesque. As for
those antique floor-cloths still occasionally seen
in the dwellings of the rabble—cloths of huge,
sprawling, and radiating devices, stripe-inter-
spersed, and glorious with all hues, among which
no ground is intelligible—these are but the

wicked invention of a race of time-savers and
money-lovers—children of Baal and worshippers
of Mammom—Benthams, who, to spare thought
and economize fancy, first cruelly invented the
Kaleidoscope, and then established joint-stock
companies to twirl it by steam.

Glare is a leading error in the philosophy of
American household decoration—an error easily
recognized as deduced from the perversion of
taste just specified. We are violently enamored
of gas and of glass. The former is totally inadmissible within doors. Its harsh and un-
steady light offends. No one having both
brains and eyes will use it. A mild, or what
artists term a cool, light, with its consequent
warm shadows, will do wonders for even an ill-
furnished apartment. Never was a more lovely
thought than that of the astral lamp. We mean,
of course, the astral lamp proper—the lamp of
Argand, with its original plain ground-glass
shade, and its tempered and uniform moonlight
rays. The cut-glass shade is a weak invention
of the enemy. The eagerness with which we
have adopted it, partly on account of its *flashi-
ness,* but principally on account of its *greater
cost,* is a good commentary on the proposition
with which we began. It is not too much to say,
that the deliberate employer of a cut-glass shade,
is either radically deficient in taste, or blindly
subservient to the caprices of fashion. The light
proceeding from one of these gaudy abomina-
tions is unequal, broken, and painful. It alone
is sufficient to mar a world of good effect in the

furniture subjected to its influence. Female loveliness, in especial, is more than one half disenchanted beneath its evil eye.

In the matter of glass, generally, we proceed upon false principles. Its leading feature is *glitter*—and in that one word how much of all that is detestable do we express! Flickering, unquiet lights, are *sometimes* pleasing—to children and idiots always so—but in the embellishment of a room they should be scrupulously avoided. In truth, even strong *steady* lights are inadmissible. The huge and unmeaning glass chandeliers, prism-cut, gas-lighted, and without shade, which dangle in our most fashionable drawing-rooms, may be cited as the quintessence of all that is false in taste or preposterous in folly.

The rage of *glitter*—because its idea has become, as we before observed, confounded with that of magnificence in the abstract—has led us, also, to the exaggerated employment of mirrors. We line our dwellings with great British plates, and then imagine we have done a fine thing. Now the slightest thought will be sufficient to convince any one who has an eye at all, of the ill effect of numerous looking-glasses, and especially of large ones. Regarded apart from its reflection, the mirror presents a continuous, flat, colorless, unrelieved surface,—a thing always and obviously unpleasant. Considered as a reflector, it is potent in producing a monstrous and odious uniformity; and the evil is here aggravated, not in merely direct proportion with the

surface of the *ground,* and thrown upon it in
such a manner as to form a succession of short
irregular curves—one occasionally overlying the
other. The walls are prepared with a glossy
paper of a silver-gray tint, spotted with small
Arabesque devices of a fainter hue of the prevalent crimson. Many paintings relieve the expanse of the paper. These are chiefly landscapes
of an imaginative cast—such as the fairy grottoes
of Stanfield, or the lake of the Dismal Swamp of
Chapman. There are, nevertheless, three or
four female heads, of an ethereal beauty—por-
traits in the manner of Sully. The tone of each
picture is warm, but dark. There are no "brilliant effects." *Repose* speaks in all. Not one
is of small size. Diminutive paintings give that
spotty look to a room, which is the blemish of
so many a fine work of Art overtouched. The
frames are broad but not deep, and richly
carved, without being *dulled* or filagreed. They
have the whole lustre of burnished gold. They
lie flat on the walls, and do not hang off with
cords. The designs themselves are often seen
to the better advantage in this latter position, but
the general appearance of the chamber is in-
jured. But one mirror—and this is not a very
large one—is visible. In shape it is nearly circular—and it is hung so that a reflection of the
person can be obtained from it in none of the
ordinary sitting-places of the room. Two large
low sofas of rosewood and crimson silk, gold-
flowered, form the only seats, with the exception
of two light conversation chairs, also of rose-

wood. There is a pianoforte (rosewood, also), without cover, and thrown open. An octagonal table, formed altogether of the richest gold-threaded marble, is placed near one of the sofas. This is also without cover—the drapery of the curtains has been thought sufficient. Four large and gorgeous Sèvres vases, in which bloom a profusion of sweet and vivid flowers, occupy the slightly rounded angles of the room. A tall candelabrum, bearing a small antique lamp with highly perfumed oil, is standing near the head of my sleeping friend. Some light and graceful hanging shelves, with golden edges and crimson silk cords with golden tassels, sustain two or three hundred magnificently bound books. Beyond these things, there is no furniture, if we except an Argand lamp, with a plain crimson-tinted ground-glass shade, which depends from the lofty vaulted ceiling by a single slender gold chain, and throws a tranquil but magical radiance over all.

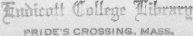